TALES OF HEARSAY
and
LAST ESSAYS

TALES OF HEARSAY
and
LAST ESSAYS

by
JOSEPH CONRAD

LONDON
J. M. DENT AND SONS LTD

A chronological list of Conrad's books,
with brief biographical details and a
list of selected writings about him,
will be found at the end of this volume.

Contents

TALES OF HEARSAY

LAST ESSAYS

CONTENTS

PREFACE

GENIUS needs no Old Mortality to clear the lichen from the letters on its tomb.

Even if the moss does gather tenderly about the stone, it only adds another grace, as traceries of frost upon a window pane render the clearest glass more beautiful.

My task is easy and I do not come to it weighed down by the sense or my inadequacy to do justice to the theme, for it will justify itself, no matter how inadequately I write.

The gulf between a man of genius and a man of talent is deeper far (width does not seem to matter) than that between a man of talent and a good craftsman working industriously upon the medium of his craft. Him we honour, partly no doubt, as says the writer of Ecclesiastes, for the need we have of him. The man of talent we admire; but genius, like the afterglow on the white cones of El Ruiz and Purace, leaves us amazed at nature's great achievement, when she puts out her strength.

When genius disappears, or when the afterglow has faded in the short tropic twilight, there comes a feeling as of a darkness in the soul.

Standing on a ship's deck, nearing the Line, when the Great Bear is setting for the last time, one knows when he has set that he has gone for good, at least, whilst that voyage lasts. Next night, although the Southern Cross is hanging overhead, we feel that there is something lacking in the sky, that all the stars, for all their brilliancy, do not make up to us.

So on the voyage of our lives, a voyage that we make in general by dead reckoning, having scant time to take an altitude, when one whom we have looked on as immortal puts on mortality and leaves us (*vagula animula!*), we feel a sense of wrong.

We know that other constellations will arise, bright, but not particular for us, will shine, and that their worshippers will fall down and adore. That will not bring back our own star to us.

Let us take consolation therefore in the hope that as the light of certain fixed stars takes a thousand years or more to reach us here, the light that has gone out on earth may yet shine brightly in some other planet, after a thousand years.

The artificial flowers, imprisoned in a shade of glass, that folks in foreign cemeteries place on the graves, have always seemed to me more suitable as emblems of the futility of grief than real flowers that fade.

They are not beautiful. Rain, wind and fog, sun and the winter's snow, the frost and hail, all the injustices that nature heaps upon them, just as fate heaped them on the men who sleep beneath the turf, blacken and disfigure, but only make them more pathetic in their stark unloveliness. Still they endure when costly wreaths have withered and decayed.

In country villages, the children put wild flowers on the graves of those they love. I write my poor exordium in the same spirit that impels the children, and makes people stick a wooden cross up in the ground, for lack of marble.

* * * * * * *

The four short stories in the book contain the first and the latest of the author's work. "The Black Mate," a sea story that he wrote about "Almayer"

Folly," must have been written about 1884, as a friend of Conrad's tells me.

The subject is half humorous and rather trifling in itself. Still it reveals the writer as a born story-teller. Strange to say, there is no evidence of immaturity in it. Conrad seems to have sprung, just as Minerva sprang, straight from Jove's brow, full armed and full equipped. His English is as perfect, perhaps more perfect, than in his latest work.

This is not so curious as it appears, for as the years roll on, a language that we have acquired in youth, when all our faculties are keen, and with the first impact that a strange tongue makes on the brain, gradually fades, and the speech that we learned at our mother's knee subconsciously reasserts itself.

The late W. H. Hudson, when I knew him first, some thirty years ago, had almost forgotten the Spanish that he had spoken daily till his eight-and-twentieth year. The last time that I saw him, he interjected sentences and words in Spanish, and in his last book "The Hind in Richmond Park," Hispaniolisms were frequent in the text. Such also was the case with Conrad. Although his flow of vigorous and idiomatic English never failed and his vocabulary only got richer as the years passed by, his accent, on the contrary, that years ago was slight, became more marked, and certain turns of phrase appeared that, though they were not English, yet gave his English grace. Accent or no accent, foreign turns of phrase or perfect English with something of greater colour and intensity in its composition than that of most born Englishmen, he was a brilliant conversationalist. Formidable in argument, to which he brought all the resources of a mind steeped in the modern literature of Europe, especially in that of France, he yet never laid down the law, or played the

Triton amongst minnows, but understood the art, as lost to-day as that of putting a keen edge upon bronze weapons, of letting each one have his say and listening courteously to what the smallest minnow in the shoal had to advance.

All his ripostes in conversation came straight off the blade "*au tic au tac*" as fencers say, when they discourse upon their mystery. His humour was so subtle that dullards generally failed to perceive that it existed and went away thinking that they had helped an interesting foreigner to face the fell corruscations of real British wit, without discrediting himself.

Still scattered through his books are passages of the subtlest and most sarcastic humour that no reviewer ever seems to have observed. Such passages as that in his great book, "Lord Jim," in which he notices the arrival of a liner at some Eastern port. He goes into the dining room and listens to the conversation of the passengers. It turns upon the donkeys that they rode at Cairo and petty scandals of the voyage. Then Conrad dismisses them to their Malebolge saying that they were as impervious to new impressions as were their trunks upstairs. Rather grim humour, but perfect of its kind, and cruel in its truth.

The story "Prince Roman," written in 1911, is laid in Poland, the only one of all his tales in which he deals directly with the country of his birth, or touches politics. Who can doubt that it is himself who speaks, in indignation at the hypocrisy of the Europe of that date, about his country's woes?—

"Of course, the year 1831 is for us an historical date, one of those fatal years, when in the presence of the world's passive indignation and eloquent sympathies, we had once more to murmur '*Væ Victis*' and count the cost in sorrow. Not that we were ever very good at calculating, either in prosperity or in adversity. That's a lesson we could never learn, to the great exasperation of our enemies who have bestowed upon us the epithet of Incorrigible. . . ."

The speaker was of Polish nationality, that nationality not so much alive as surviving, which persists in thinking, breathing, speaking, hoping and suffering in its grave, railed in by a million of bayonets and triple-sealed with the seals of three great empires.

That speaker's name was Joseph Conrad Korzeniowski without doubt. In every word there breathes the spirit of the Polish patriot, the burning sense of wrong, and of resentment at the hypocrisy of Europe that looked on "sympathizing eloquently," with all his country's wrongs.

Further on he says:

It requires a certain greatness of soul to interpret patriotism worthily—or else a sincerity of feeling denied to the vulgar refinement of modern thought which cannot understand the august simplicity of a sentiment proceeding from the very nature of things and men.

"Vulgar refinement" is good. We are suffocated with it. One feels that all the bitterness that he must have endured so stoically, for he surely spoke of Poland or her lot, had broken out at last, just as a volcano, long quiescent, one day bursts forth, and carries everything before it in a molten stream, straight from the bowels of the earth. The outburst has more force, if only from the fact that, as far as I know, it was the one occasion in his literary career that he allowed it vent.

This single ebullition from a man usually so self-contained, written in his study and not mouthed out before a crowd with all the antics of an orator, gives us a real insight into his character. Poland indeed, in 1911, was the Cinderella of the nations, sitting amongst the ashes, outraged, mocked at, and oppressed and crucified between the three great empires who with their triple seal held her in servitude. He lived to see her free and take her place again amongst the nations of the world. The curious story Conrad no doubt heard in childhood, and retained it in his tenacious memory that let nothing slip that he had heard.

Scattered through the tale are passages evidently descriptive of the house where he was born. The "great stone-paved hall, warmed by a monumental stove of white tiles" so much more comfortable "than the schoolroom" that was "always kept at a low temperature," the groom lighting the coach to the stables, carrying "a blazing ball of tow and resin in an iron basket at the end of a long stick swung from his saddle bow," all speak of memories of his youth.

If he had retained these recollections of the house, his memories of the landscape were not less acute, as "far away to the north the great Lithuanian forest faced the sun, no higher than a hedge." This, and his childish interest in a certain wolf that had been committing depredations in the neighbourhood, show how deeply all the surroundings of his childhood's home had remained vivid in his mind. His hatred of the Russians shows itself in passages such as the following:

Emperor Nicholas, who always took personal cognizance of all sentences on the Polish nobility, wrote with his own hand on the margin, "The authorities are severely warned to take care that this convict walks in chains (to Siberia) like any other criminal, every step of the way."

Emperors and kings have written many foolish things on margins of dispatches and the like, as when Philip II of Spain wrote on the margin of a dispatch he had received from England, telling amongst other things (perhaps of lesser import) of a plague of lice that had broken out in Whitehall, "Quizas eran pulgas," "Perhaps they were fleas."

Seldom has the hatred of a tyrant expressed itself more venomously than in the marginal note that Conrad quotes. This story lets us see clearly how much his country's wrongs at the hands of Russian tyrants was on his mind. He seldom spoke upon such matters, but I am glad he gave full rein to his feelings in this most interesting tale.

The third story on the list is called "The Tale." He must have heard it from some sailor in the war, probably badly told in skeleton.

As Shakespeare often took episodes from Holinshed and with his magic pen gave them both brilliancy and life, so Conrad dealt with this sailor's yarn and left it glorified.

Just as in "Typhoon" he puts into words what many have experienced, so in "The Tale" he takes the familiar episode of a ship fogbound off a dangerous coast in wartime, and makes the reader stand trembling as the vessel noses her way, as if by instinct, into the deserted creek. We do not only see and feel the fog, but it gets down our throats, makes our eyes smart, confuses all our senses and makes us understand the state of mind of the American who naïvely said to him, "Say, Mr. Conrad, how in thunder did it come into your head?"

This tale and the next, "The Warrior's Soul," were written in 1917. They show his genius ever maturing, never looking back, as fresh and powerful as when, many years ago, he wrote those masterpieces, "The Heart of Darkness," "Youth," and "The Mirror of the Sea."

Few stories in the language are as dramatic as "The Warrior's Soul." It is well worthy of a place beside Hudson's "El Ombu" and "Wandering Willie's Tale."

The Sheriff, master mariner, and Gaucho, naturalist, meet and join hands, for genius overlaps all barriers, whether of time, or speech or nationality, and makes men kin to one another, who perchance would have been poles asunder when they were alive.

In the remarkable and most dramatic story, "The Warrior's Soul," the writer seems to have put forth all his powers as a short story writer. It is, in fact, a sort of swan song, for though he added to his laurels with his last book "The Rover," as regards the short story, when he had written the last pages of "The Warrior's Soul" he laid the lyre aside for good.

Of all the purely hearsay tales he ever wrote perhaps "The Warrior's Soul" holds the first place. I can imagine him, in the old homestead that he describes with so much love and such artistic skill in his sketch "Poland Revisited," seated before the enormous china stove upon a winter's night, the pine trees standing up starkly out of the white ocean, as palm trees stand up out of the desert sand, but black and withered, their branches weighed down by the snow.

Now and then a wolf would howl, with that long-drawn-out melancholy sound that, once heard, especially when one is alone, far from a human habitation, is never to be forgotten, making him cower to his mother's side, as some one told the story that he has so splendidly dressed up and made live.

In it he rises above nationality, even his hatred of the hereditary tyrants of his country is forgotten. He sees them with their country laid waste and invaded by the Napoleonic hordes, and as he understood by dire experience, what they were passing through gives them his sympathy. No light thing for a Pole to do, and one that in itself shows him a man of genius on another side, for it wants genius to feel for the oppressor in his hour of need. To feel for the oppressed, that we can all do easily enough. All Conrad's art, his skill in drawing character, his ear for curious locutions, such as "simple servants of God" to express country people, are to be found in this amazing tale. The horror of the great retreat from Moscow seems to have been observed by an eye witness. Still it is but a hearsay tale, heard in his youth, and written in his later years when his thoughts turned again to old familiar things.

Nothing that I know of in any of his shorter stories equals the dramatic ending of "The Warrior's Soul."

Horror and misery can go no further than the scene where the French officer, staring and spectrelike, walks into the Russian lines, and asks Tomassov, whose life he once had saved in Paris, to pay the debt off with a pistol shot, and end his misery.

In all the stories, even in the first, written before he had fairly found his wings, there is a vein of great urbanity and knowledge of the world, for Conrad never preaches, but only holds the mirror up to nature, for men to see themselves, and draw such moral as they can, from their own faces

* * * * * * *

There is a fountain in Marrakesh with a palm tree near it, a gem of Moorish art, with tiles as iridescent as the scales upon a lizard's back.

Written in Cufic characters, there is this legend, "Drink and admire."

Read and admire; then return thanks to Allah who gives water to the thirsty and at long intervals sends us refreshment for the soul.

R. B. CUNNINGHAME GRAHAM.

NOTE

THE title chosen for this book, "TALES OF HEARSAY," is one which Conrad long had in his mind for a future volume of short stories. As it fits very well the four stories included here it has been deemed proper to give the title which had Conrad's own authority.

TALES OF HEARSAY

THE WARRIOR'S SOUL

THE old officer with long white moustaches gave rein to his indignation.

"Is it possible that you youngsters should have no more sense than that! Some of you had better wipe the milk off your upper lip before you start to pass judgment on the few poor stragglers of a generation which has done and suffered not a little in its time."

His hearers having expressed much compunction the ancient warrior became appeased. But he was not silenced.

"I am one of them—one of the stragglers, I mean," he went on patiently. "And what did we do? What have we achieved? He—the great Napoleon—started upon us to emulate the Macedonian Alexander, with a ruck of nations at his back. We opposed empty spaces to French impetuosity, then we offered them an interminable battle so that their army went at last to sleep in its positions lying down on the heaps of its own dead. Then came the wall of fire in Moscow. It toppled down on them.

"Then began the long rout of the Grand Army. I have seen it stream on, like the doomed flight of haggard, spectral sinners across the innermost frozen circle of Dante's Inferno, ever widening before their despairing eyes.

1

"They who escaped must have had their souls doubly riveted inside their bodies to carry them out of Russia through that frost fit to split rocks. But to say that it was our fault that a single one of them got away is mere ignorance. Why! Our own men suffered nearly to the limit of their strength. Their Russian strength!

"Of course our spirit was not broken; and then our cause was good—it was holy. But that did not temper the wind much to men and horses.

"The flesh is weak. Good or evil purpose, Humanity has to pay the price. Why! In that very fight for that little village of which I have been telling you we were fighting for the shelter of those old houses as much as victory. And with the French it was the same.

"It wasn't for the sake of glory, or for the sake of strategy. The French knew that they would have to retreat before morning and we knew perfectly well that they would go. As far as the war was concerned there was nothing to fight about. Yet our infantry and theirs fought like wild cats, or like heroes if you like that better, amongst the houses—hot work enough—while the supports out in the open stood freezing in a tempestuous north wind which drove the snow on earth and the great masses of clouds in the sky at a terrific pace. The very air was inexpressibly sombre by contrast with the white earth. I have never seen God's creation look more sinister than on that day.

"We, the cavalry (we were only a handful), had not much to do except turn our backs to the wind and receive some stray French round shot. This, I may tell you, was the last of the French guns and it was the last time they had their artillery in position. Those guns never went away from there either. We found them abandoned next morning. But that afternoon they were keeping up an infernal fire on our attacking column; the furious wind carried away the smoke and even the noise but we could see the constant flicker of the tongues of fire along the French front. Then a driving flurry of snow would hide everything except the dark red flashes in the white swirl.

"At intervals when the line cleared we could see away across the plain to the right a sombre column moving endlessly; the great rout of the Grand Army creeping on and on all the time while the fight on our left went on with a great din and fury. The cruel whirlwind of snow swept over that scene of death and desolation. And then the wind fell as suddenly as it had arisen in the morning.

"Presently we got orders to charge the retreating column; I don't know why unless they wanted to prevent us from getting frozen in our saddles by giving us something to do. We changed front half right and got into motion at a walk to take that distant dark line in flank. It might have been half-past two in the afternoon.

"You must know that so far in this campaign my regiment had never been on the main line of Napoleon's advance. All these months since the invasion the army we belonged to had been wrestling with Oudinot in the north. We had only come down lately, driving him before us to the Beresina.

"This was the first occasion, then, that I and my comrades had a close view of Napoleon's Grand Army. It was an amazing and terrible sight. I had heard of it from others; I had seen the stragglers from it: small bands of marauders, parties of prisoners in the distance. But this was the very column itself! A crawling, stumbling, starved, half-demented mob. It issued from the forest a mile away and its head was lost in the murk of the fields. We rode into it at a trot, which was the most we could get out of our horses, and we stuck in that human mass as if in a moving bog. There was no resistance. I heard a few shots, half a dozen perhaps. Their very senses seemed frozen within them. I had time for a good look while riding at the head of my squadron. Well, I assure you, there were men walking on the outer edge so lost to everything but their misery that they never turned their heads to look at our charge. Soldiers!

"My horse pushed over one of them with his chest. The poor wretch had a dragoon's blue cloak, all torn and scorched, hanging from his shoulders and he didn't even put his hand out to snatch at my bridle and save himself. He just went down. Our troopers were pointing and slashing; well, and of course at first I myself . . . What would you have! An enemy is an enemy. Yet a sort of sickening awe crept into my heart. There was no tumult—only a low deep murmur dwelt over them interspersed with louder cries and groans while that mob kept on pushing and surging past us, sightless and without feeling. A smell of scorched rags and festering wounds hung in the air. My horse staggered in the eddies of swaying men. But it was like cutting down galvanized corpses that didn't care. Invaders! Yes . . . God was already dealing with them.

"I touched my horse with the spurs to get clear. There was a sudden rush and a sort of angry moan when our second squadron got into them on our right. My horse plunged and somebody got hold of my leg. As I had no mind to get pulled out of the saddle I gave a back-handed slash without looking. I heard a cry and my leg was let go suddenly.

"Just then I caught sight of the subaltern of my troop at some little distance from me. His name was Tomassov. That multitude of resurrected bodies with glassy eyes was seething round his horse as if blind, growling crazily. He was sitting erect in his saddle, not looking down at them and sheathing his sword deliberately.

"This Tomassov, well, he had a beard. Of course we all had beards then. Circumstances, lack of leisure, want of razors, too. No, seriously, we were a wild-looking lot in those unforgotten days which so many, so very many of us did not survive. You know our losses were awful, too. Yes, we looked wild. *Des Russes sauvages*—what!

"So he had a beard—this Tomassov I mean; but he did not look *sauvage*. He was the youngest of us all. And that meant real youth. At a distance he passed muster fairly well, what with the grime and the particular stamp of that campaign on our faces. But directly you were near enough to have a good look into his eyes, that was where his lack of age showed, though he was not exactly a boy.

"Those same eyes were blue, something like the blue of autumn skies, dreamy and gay, too—innocent, believing eyes. A topknot of fair hair decorated his brow like a gold diadem in what one would call normal times.

"You may think I am talking of him as if he were the hero of a novel. Why, that's nothing to what the adjutant discovered about him. He discovered that he had a 'lover's lips'—whatever that may be. If the adjutant meant a nice mouth, why, it was nice enough, but of course it was intended for a sneer. That adjutant of ours was not a very delicate fellow. 'Look at those lover's lips,' he would exclaim in a loud tone while Tomassov was talking.

"Tomassov didn't quite like that sort of thing. But to a certain extent he had laid himself open to banter by the lasting character of his impressions which were connected with the passion of love and, perhaps, were not of such a rare kind as he seemed to think them. What made his comrades tolerant of his rhapsodies was the fact that they were connected with France, with Paris!

"You of the present generation, you cannot conceive how much prestige there was then in those names for the whole world. Paris was the centre of wonder for all human beings gifted with imagination. There we were, the majority of us young and well connected, but not long out of our hereditary nests in the provinces; simple servants of God; mere rustics, if I may say so. So we were only too ready to listen to the tales of France from our comrade Tomassov. He had been attached to our mission in Paris the year before the war. High protections very likely—or maybe sheer luck.

"I don't think he could have been a very useful member of the mission because of his youth and complete inexperience. And apparently all his time in Paris was his own. The use he made of it was to fall in love, to remain in that state, to cultivate it, to exist only for it in a manner of speaking.

"Thus it was something more than a mere memory that he had brought with him from France. Memory is a fugitive thing. It can be falsified, it can be effaced, it can be even doubted. Why! I myself come to doubt sometimes that I, too, have been in Paris in my turn. And the long road there with battles for its stages would appear still more incredible if it were not for a certain musket ball which I have been carrying about my person ever since a little cavalry affair which happened in Silesia at the very beginning of the Leipsic campaign.

"Passages of love, however, are more impressive perhaps than passages of danger. You don't go affronting love in troops as it were. They are rarer, more personal and more intimate. And remember that with Tomassov all that was very fresh yet. He had not been home from France three months when the war began.

"His heart, his mind were full of that experience. He was really awed by it, and he was simple enough to let it appear in his speeches. He considered himself a sort of privileged person, not because a woman had looked at him with favour, but simply because, how shall I say it, he had had the wonderful illumination of his worship for her, as if it were heaven itself that had done this for him.

"Oh yes, he was very simple. A nice youngster, yet no fool; and with that, utterly inexperienced, unsuspicious, and unthinking. You will find one like that here and there in the provinces. He had some poetry in him too. It could only be natural, something quite his own, not acquired. I suppose Father Adam had some poetry in him of that natural sort. For the rest *un Russe sauvage* as the French sometimes call us, but not of that kind which, they maintain, eats tallow candle for a delicacy. As to the woman, the French woman, well, though I have also been in France with a hundred thousand Russians, I have never seen her. Very likely she was not in Paris then. And in any case hers were not the doors that would fly open before simple fellows of my sort, you understand. Gilded salons were never in my way. I could not tell you how she looked, which is strange considering that I was, if I may say so, Tomassov's special confidant.

"He very soon got shy of talking before the others. I suppose the usual camp-fire comments jarred his fine feelings. But I was left to him and truly I had to submit. You can't very well expect a youngster in Tomassov's state to hold his tongue altogether; and I—I suppose you will hardly believe me—I am by nature a rather silent sort of person.

"Very likely my silence appeared to him sympathetic. All the month of September our regiment, quartered in villages, had come in for an easy time. It was then that I heard most of that—you can't call it a story. The story I have in my mind is not in that. Out-pourings, let us call them.

"I would sit quite content to hold my peace, a whole hour perhaps, while Tomassov talked with exaltation. And when he was done I would still hold my peace. And then there would be produced a solemn effect of silence which, I imagine, pleased Tomassov in a way.

"She was of course not a woman in her first youth. A widow, maybe. At any rate I never heard Tomassov mention her husband. She had a salon, something very distinguished; a social centre in which she queened it with great splendour.

"Somehow, I fancy her court was composed mostly of men. But Tomassov, I must say, kept such details out of his discourses wonderfully well. Upon my word I don't know whether her hair was dark or fair, her eyes brown or blue; what was her stature, her features, or her complexion. His love soared above mere physical impressions. He never described her to me in set terms; but he was ready to swear that in her presence everybody's thoughts and feelings were bound to circle round her. She was that sort of woman. Most wonderful conversations on all sorts of subjects went on in her salon: but through them all there flowed unheard like a mysterious strain of music the assertion, the power, the tyranny of sheer beauty. So apparently the woman was beautiful. She detached all these talking people from their life interests, and even from their vanities. She was a secret delight and a secret trouble. All the men when they looked at her fell to brooding as if struck by the thought that their lives had been wasted. She was the very joy and shudder of felicity and she brought only sadness and torment to the hearts of men.

"In short, she must have been an extraordinary woman, or else Tomassov was an extraordinary young fellow to feel in that way and to talk like this about her. I told you the fellow had a lot of poetry in him and observed that all this sounded true enough. It would be just about the sorcery a woman very much out of the common would exercise, you know. Poets do get close to truth somehow—there is no denying that.

"There is no poetry in my composition, I know, but I have my share of common shrewdness, and I have no doubt that the lady was kind to the youngster, once he did find his way inside her salon. His getting in is the real marvel. However, he did get in, the innocent, and he found himself in distinguished company there, amongst men of considerable position. And you know what that means: thick waists, bald heads, teeth that are not—as some satirist puts it. Imagine amongst them a nice boy, fresh and simple, like an apple just off the tree; a modest, good-looking, impressionable, adoring young barbarian. My word! What a change! What a relief for jaded feelings! And with that, having in his nature that dose of poetry which saves even a simpleton from being a fool.

"He became an artlessly, unconditionally devoted slave. He was rewarded by being smiled on and in time admitted to the intimacy of the house. It may be that the unsophisticated young barbarian amused the exquisite lady. Perhaps—since he didn't feed on tallow candles—he satisfied some need of tenderness in

the woman. You know, there are many kinds of
tenderness highly civilized women are capable of.
Women with heads and imagination, I mean, and no
temperament to speak of, you understand. But who
is going to fathom their needs or their fancies? Most
of the time they themselves don't know much about
their innermost moods, and blunder out of one into another, sometimes with catastrophic results. And
then who is more surprised than they? However,
Tomassov's case was in its nature quite idyllic. The
fashionable world was amused. His devotion made
for him a kind of social success. But he didn't care.
There was his one divinity, and there was the shrine
where he was permitted to go in and out without regard
for official reception hours.

"He took advantage of that privilege freely. Well,
he had no official duties, you know. The Military
Mission was supposed to be more complimentary than
anything else, the head of it being a personal friend of
our Emperor Alexander; and he, too, was laying himself
out for successes in fashionable life exclusively—as it
seemed. As it seemed.

"One afternoon Tomassov called on the mistress of
his thoughts earlier than usual. She was not alone.
There was a man with her, not one of the thick-waisted,
bald-headed personages, but a somebody all the same,
a man over thirty, a French officer who to some extent
was also a privileged intimate. Tomassov was not
jealous of him. Such a sentiment would have appeared
presumptuous to the simple fellow.

"On the contrary he admired that officer. You have
no idea of the French military men's prestige in those
days, even with us Russian soldiers who had managed
to face them perhaps better than the rest. Victory
had marked them on the forehead—it seemed for ever.

They would have been more than human if they had not been conscious of it; but they were good comrades and had a sort of brotherly feeling for all who bore arms, even if it was against them.

"And this was quite a superior example, an officer of the major-general's staff, and a man of the best society besides. He was powerfully built, and thoroughly masculine, though he was as carefully groomed as a woman. He had the courteous self-possession of a man of the world. His forehead, white as alabaster, contrasted impressively with the healthy colour of his face.

"I don't know whether he was jealous of Tomassov, but I suspect that he might have been a little annoyed at him as at a sort of walking absurdity of the sentimental order. But these men of the world are impenetrable, and outwardly he condescended to recognize Tomassov's existence even more distinctly than was strictly necessary. Once or twice he had offered him some useful worldly advice with perfect tact and delicacy. Tomassov was completely conquered by that evidence of kindness under the cold polish of the best society.

"Tomassov, introduced into the *petit salon*, found these two exquisite people sitting on a sofa together and had the feeling of having interrupted some special conversation. They looked at him strangely, he thought; but he was not given to understand that he had intruded. After a time the lady said to the officer—his name was De Castel—'I wish you would take the trouble to ascertain the exact truth as to that rumour.'

"'It's much more than a mere rumour,' remarked the officer. But he got up submissively and went out. The lady turned to Tomassov and said: 'You may stay with me.'

"This express command made him supremely happy, though as a matter of fact he had had no idea of going.

"She regarded him with her kindly glances, which made something glow and expand within his chest. It was a delicious feeling, even though it did cut one's breath short now and then. Ecstatically he drank in the sound of her tranquil, seductive talk full of innocent gaiety and of spiritual quietude. His passion appeared to him to flame up and envelop her in blue fiery tongues from head to foot and over her head, while her soul reposed in the centre like a big white rose. . . .

"H'm, good this. He told me many other things like that. But this is the one I remember. He himself remembered everything because these were the last memories of that woman. He was seeing her for the last time though he did not know it then.

"M. De Castel returned, breaking into that atmosphere of enchantment Tomassov had been drinking in even to complete unconsciousness of the external world. Tomassov could not help being struck by the distinction of his movements, the ease of his manner, his superiority to all the other men he knew, and he suffered from it. It occurred to him that these two brilliant beings on the sofa were made for each other.

"De Castel sitting down by the side of the lady murmured to her discreetly, 'There is not the slightest doubt that it's true,' and they both turned their eyes to Tomassov. Roused thoroughly from his enchantment he became self-conscious; a feeling of shyness came over him. He sat smiling faintly at them.

"The lady without taking her eyes off the blushing Tomassov said with a dreamy gravity quite unusual to her:

"'I should like to know that your generosity can be

supreme—without a flaw. Love at its highest should be the origin of every perfection.'

"Tomassov opened his eyes wide with admiration at this, as though her lips had been dropping real pearls. The sentiment, however, was not uttered for the primitive Russian youth but for the exquisitely accomplished man of the world, De Castel.

"Tomassov could not see the effect it produced because the French officer lowered his head and sat there contemplating his admirably polished boots. The lady whispered in a sympathetic tone:

"'You have scruples?'

"De Castel, without looking up, murmured: 'It could be turned into a nice point of honour.'

"She said vivaciously: 'That surely is artificial. I am all for natural feelings. I believe in nothing else. But perhaps your conscience . . .'

"He interrupted her: 'Not at all. My conscience is not childish. The fate of those people is of no military importance to us. What can it matter? The fortune of France is invincible.'

"'Well then . . .' she uttered, meaningly, and rose from the couch. The French officer stood up, too. Tomassov hastened to follow their example. He was pained by his state of utter mental darkness. While he was raising the lady's white hand to his lips he heard the French officer say with marked emphasis:

"'If he has the soul of a warrior (at that time, you know, people really talked in that way), if he has the soul of a warrior he ought to fall at your feet in gratitude.'

"Tomassov felt himself plunged into even denser darkness than before. He followed the French officer out of the room and out of the house; for he had a notion that this was expected of him.

"It was getting dusk, the weather was very bad, and the street was quite deserted. The Frenchman lingered in it strangely. And Tomassov lingered, too, without impatience. He was never in a hurry to get away from the house in which she lived. And besides, something wonderful had happened to him. The hand he had reverently raised by the tips of its fingers had been pressed against his lips. He had received a secret favour! He was almost frightened. The world had reeled—and it had hardly steadied itself yet. De Castel stopped short at the corner of the quiet street.

"'I don't care to be seen too much with you in the lighted thoroughfares, M. Tomassov,' he said in a strangely grim tone.

"'Why?' asked the young man, too startled to be offended.

"'From prudence,' answered the other curtly. 'So we will have to part here; but before we part I'll disclose to you something of which you will see at once the importance.'

"This, please note, was an evening in late March of the year 1812. For a long time already there had been talk of a growing coolness between Russia and France. The word war was being whispered in drawing rooms louder and louder, and at last was heard in official circles. Thereupon the Parisian police discovered that our military envoy had corrupted some clerks at the Ministry of War and had obtained from them some very important confidential documents. The wretched men (there were two of them) had confessed their crime and were to be shot that night. To-morrow all the town would be talking of the affair. But the worst was that the Emperor Napoleon was furiously angry at the discovery, and had made up his mind to have the Russian envoy arrested.

"Such was De Castel's disclosure; and though he had spoken in low tones Tomassov was stunned as by a great crash.

"'Arrested,' he murmured, desolately.

"'Yes, and kept as a state prisoner—with everybody belonging to him. . . .'

"The French officer seized Tomassov's arm above the elbow and pressed it hard.

"'And kept in France,' he repeated into Tomassov's very ear, and then letting him go stepped back a space and remained silent.

"'And it's you, you, who are telling me this!' cried Tomassov in an extremity of gratitude that was hardly greater than his admiration for the generosity of his future foe. Could a brother have done for him more! He sought to seize the hand of the French officer, but the latter remained wrapped up closely in his cloak. Possibly in the dark he had not noticed the attempt. He moved back a bit and in his self-possessed voice of a man of the world, as though he were speaking across a card table or something of the sort, he called Tomassov's attention to the fact that if he meant to make use of the warning the moments were precious.

"'Indeed they are,' agreed the awed Tomassov. 'Good-bye then. I have no word of thanks to equal your generosity; but if ever I have an opportunity, I swear it, you may command my life. . . .'

"But the Frenchman retreated, had already vanished in the dark lonely street. Tomassov was alone, and then he did not waste any of the precious minutes of that night.

"See how people's mere gossip and idle talk pass into history. In all the memoirs of the time if you read them you will find it stated that our envoy had a warning from some highly placed woman who was in love with him. Of course it's known that he had successes with women, and in the highest spheres, too, but the truth is that the person who warned him was no other than our simple Tomassov—an altogether different sort of lover from himself.

"This then is the secret of our Emperor's representative's escape from arrest. He and all his official household got out of France all right—as history records.

"And amongst that household there was our Tomassov of course. He had, in the words of the French officer, the soul of a warrior. And what more desolate prospect for a man with such a soul than to be imprisoned on the eve of war; to be cut off from his country in danger, from his military family, from his duty, from honour, and—well—from glory, too.

"Tomassov used to shudder at the mere thought of the moral torture he had escaped; and he nursed in his heart a boundless gratitude to the two people who had saved him from that cruel ordeal. They were wonderful! For him love and friendship were but two aspects of exalted perfection. He had found these fine examples of it and he vowed them indeed a sort of cult. It affected his attitude towards Frenchmen in general, great patriot as he was. He was naturally indignant at the invasion of his country, but this indignation had no personal animosity in it. His was fundamentally a fine nature. He grieved at the appalling amount of human suffering he saw around him. Yes, he was full of compassion for all forms of mankind's misery in a manly way.

"Less fine natures than his own did not understand this very well. In the regiment they had nicknamed him the Humane Tomassov.

"He didn't take offence at it. There is nothing incompatible between humanity and a warrior's soul. People without compassion are the civilians, government officials, merchants and such like. As to the ferocious talk one hears from a lot of decent people in war time—well, the tongue is an unruly member at best, and when there is some excitement going on there is no curbing its furious activity.

"So I had not been very surprised to see our Tomassov sheathe deliberately his sword right in the middle of that charge, you may say. As we rode away after it he was very silent. He was not a chatterer as a rule, but it was evident that this close view of the Grand Army had affected him deeply, like some sight not of this earth. I had always been a pretty tough individual myself—well, even I . . . and there was that fellow with a lot of poetry in his nature! You may imagine what he made of it to himself. We rode side by side without opening our lips. It was simply beyond words.

"We established our bivouac along the edge of the forest so as to get some shelter for our horses. However, the boisterous north wind had dropped as quickly as it had sprung up, and the great winter stillness lay on the land from the Baltic to the Black Sea. One could almost feel its cold, lifeless immensity reaching up to the stars.

"Our men had lighted several fires for their officers and had cleared the snow around them. We had big logs of wood for seats; it was a very tolerable bivouac upon the whole, even without the exultation of victory. We were to feel that later, but at present we were oppressed by our stern and arduous task.

"There were three of us round my fire. The third one was that adjutant. He was perhaps a well-meaning chap but not so nice as he might have been had he been

B

less rough in manner and less crude in his perceptions. He would reason about people's conduct as though a man were as simple a figure as, say, two sticks laid across each other; whereas a man is much more like the sea whose movements are too complicated to explain, and whose depths may bring up God only knows what at any moment.

"We talked a little about that charge. Not much. That sort of thing does not lend itself to conversation. Tomassov muttered a few words about a mere butchery. I had nothing to say. As I told you I had very soon let my sword hang idle at my wrist. That starving mob had not even *tried* to defend itself. Just a few shots. We had two men wounded. Two! . . . and we had charged the main column of Napoleon's Grand Army.

"Tomassov muttered wearily: 'What was the good of it?' I did not wish to argue, so I only just mumbled: 'Ah, well!' But the adjutant struck in unpleasantly:

"'Why, it warmed the men a bit. It has made me warm. That's a good enough reason. But our Tomassov is so humane! And besides he has been in love with a French woman, and thick as thieves with a lot of Frenchmen, so he is sorry for them. Never mind, my boy, we are on the Paris road now and you shall soon see her!' This was one of his usual, as we believed them, foolish speeches. None of us but believed that the getting to Paris would be a matter of years—of years. And lo! less than eighteen months afterwards I was rooked of a lot of money in a gambling hell in the Palais Royal.

"Truth, being often the most senseless thing in the world, is sometimes revealed to fools. I don't think that adjutant of ours believed in his own words. He just wanted to tease Tomassov from habit. Purely from habit. We of course said nothing, and so he took his head in his hands and fell into a doze as he sat on a log in front of the fire.

"Our cavalry was on the extreme right wing of the army, and I must confess that we guarded it very badly. We had lost all sense of insecurity by this time; but still we did keep up a pretence of doing it in a way. Presently a trooper rode up leading a horse and Tomassov mounted stiffly and went off on a round of the outposts. Of the perfectly useless outposts.

"The night was still, except for the crackling of the fires. The raging wind had lifted far above the earth and not the faintest breath of it could be heard. Only the full moon swam out with a rush into the sky and suddenly hung high and motionless overhead. I remember raising my hairy face to it for a moment. Then, I verily believe, I dozed off, too, bent double on my log with my head towards the fierce blaze.

"You know what an impermanent thing such slumber is. One moment you drop into an abyss and the next you are back in the world that you would think too deep for any noise but the trumpet of the Last Judgment. And then off you go again. Your very soul seems to slip down into a bottomless black pit. Then up once more into a startled consciousness. A mere plaything of cruel sleep one is, then. Tormented both ways.

"However, when my orderly appeared before me, repeating: 'Won't your Honour be pleased to eat? . . . Won't your Honour be pleased to eat? . . .' I managed to keep my hold of it—I mean that gaping consciousness. He was offering me a sooty pot containing some grain boiled in water with a pinch of salt. A wooden spoon was stuck in it.

"At that time these were the only rations we were

getting regularly. Mere chicken food, confound it! But the Russian soldier is wonderful. Well, my fellow waited till I had feasted and then went away carrying off the empty pot.

"I was no longer sleepy. Indeed, I had become awake with an exaggerated mental consciousness of existence extending beyond my immediate surroundings. Those are but exceptional moments with mankind, I am glad to say. I had the intimate sensation of the earth in all its enormous expanse wrapped in snow, with nothing showing on it but trees with their straight stalk-like trunks and their funeral verdure; and in this aspect of general mourning I seemed to hear the sighs of mankind falling to die in the midst of a nature without life. They were Frenchmen. We didn't hate them; they did not hate us; we had existed far apart—and suddenly they had come rolling in with arms in their hands, without fear of God, carrying with them other nations, and all to perish together in a long, long trail of frozen corpses. I had an actual vision of that trail: a pathetic multitude of small dark mounds stretching away under the moonlight in a clear, still, and pitiless atmosphere—a sort of horrible peace.

"But what other peace could there be for them? What else did they deserve? I don't know by what connection of emotions there came into my head the thought that the earth was a pagan planet and not a fit abode for Christian virtues.

"You may be surprised that I should remember all this so well. What is a passing emotion or half-formed thought to last in so many years of a man's changing inconsequential life? But what has fixed the emotion of that evening in my recollection so that the slightest shadows remain indelible was an event of strange

finality, an event not likely to be forgotten in a life-time
—as you shall see.

"I don't suppose I had been entertaining those
thoughts more than five minutes when something induced me to look over my shoulder. I can't think it
was a noise; the snow deadened all the sounds. Something it must have been, some sort of signal reaching my
consciousness. Anyway, I turned my head, and there
was the event approaching me, not that I knew it or
had the slightest premonition. All I saw in the distance were two figures approaching in the moonlight.
One of them was our Tomassov. The dark mass
behind him which moved across my sight were the
horses which his orderly was leading away. Tomassov
was a very familiar appearance, in long boots, a tall
figure ending in a pointed hood. But by his side advanced another figure. I mistrusted my eyes at first.
It was amazing! It had a shining crested helmet on its
head and was muffled up in a white cloak. The cloak
was not as white as snow. Nothing in the world is.
It was white more like mist, with an aspect that was
ghostly and martial to an extraordinary degree. It
was as if Tomassov had got hold of the God of War himself. I could see at once that he was leading this re-
splendent vision by the arm. Then I saw that he was
holding it up. While I stared and stared, they crept
on—for indeed they were creeping—and at last they
crept into the light of our bivouac fire and passed beyond the log I was sitting on. The blaze played on the
helmet. It was extremely battered and the frost-bitten
face, full of sores, under it was framed in bits of mangy
fur. No God of War this, but a French officer. The
great white cuirassier's cloak was torn, burnt full of holes.
His feet were wrapped up in old sheepskins over rem-
ants of boots. They looked monstrous and he tot-

tered on them, sustained by Tomassov who lowered him most carefully on to the log on which I sat.

"My amazement knew no bounds.

"'You have brought in a prisoner,' I said to Tomassov, as if I could not believe my eyes.

"You must understand that unless they surrendered in large bodies we made no prisoners. What would have been the good? Our Cossacks either killed the stragglers or else let them alone, just as it happened. It came really to the same thing in the end.

"Tomassov turned to me with a very troubled look.

"'He sprang up from the ground somewhere as I was leaving the outpost,' he said. 'I believe he was making for it, for he walked blindly into my horse. He got hold of my leg and of course none of our chaps dared touch him then.'

"'He had a narrow escape,' I said.

"'He didn't appreciate it,' said Tomassov, looking even more troubled than before. 'He came along holding to my stirrup leather. That's what made me so late. He told me he was a staff officer; and then talking in a voice such, I suppose, as the damned alone use, a croaking of rage and pain, he said he had a favour to beg of me. A supreme favour. Did I understand him, he asked in a sort of fiendish whisper.

"'Of course I told him that I did. I said: *oui, je vous comprends.*'

"'Then,' said he, 'do it. Now! At once—in the pity of your heart.'

"Tomassov ceased and stared queerly at me above the head of the prisoner.

"I said, 'What did he mean?'

"'That's what I asked him,' answered Tomassov in a dazed tone, 'and he said that he wanted me to do him the favour to blow his brains out. As a fellow soldier,' he said. 'As a man of feeling—as—as a humane man.'

"The prisoner sat between us like an awful gashed mummy as to the face, a martial scarecrow, a grotesque horror of rags and dirt, with awful living eyes, full of vitality, full of unquenchable fire, in a body of horrible affliction, a skeleton at the feast of glory. And suddenly those shining unextinguishable eyes of his became fixed upon Tomassov. He, poor fellow, fascinated, returned the ghastly stare of a suffering soul in that mere husk of a man. The prisoner croaked at him in French.

"'I recognize, you know. You are her Russian youngster. You were very grateful. I call on you to pay the debt. Pay it, I say, with one liberating shot. You are a man of honour. I have not even a broken sabre. All my being recoils from my own degradation. You know me.'

"Tomassov said nothing.

"'Haven't you got the soul of a warrior?' the Frenchman asked in an angry whisper, but with something of a mocking intention in it.

"'I don't know,' said poor Tomassov.

"What a look of contempt that scarecrow gave him out of his unquenchable eyes. He seemed to live only by the force of infuriated and impotent despair. Suddenly he gave a gasp and fell forward writhing in the agony of cramp in all his limbs; a not unusual effect of the heat of a camp-fire. It resembled the application of some horrible torture. But he tried to fight against the pain at first. He only moaned low while we bent over him so as to prevent him rolling into the fire, and muttered feverishly at intervals: '*Tuez moi, tuez moi* . . .' till, vanquished by the pain, he screamed in agony, time after time, each cry bursting out through his compressed lips.

"The adjutant woke up on the other side of the fire and started swearing awfully at the beastly row that Frenchman was making.

"'What's this? More of your infernal humanity, Tomassov,' he yelled at us. 'Why don't you have him thrown out of this to the devil on the snow?'

"As we paid no attention to his shouts, he got up, cursing shockingly, and went away to another fire. Presently the French officer became easier. We propped him up against the log and sat silent on each side of him till the bugles started their call at the first break of day. The big flame, kept up all through the night, paled on the livid sheet of snow, while the frozen air all round rang with the brazen notes of cavalry trumpets. The Frenchman's eyes, fixed in a glassy stare, which for a moment made us hope that he had died quietly sitting there between us two, stirred slowly to right and left, looking at each of our faces in turn. Tomassov and I exchanged glances of dismay. Then De Castel's voice, unexpected in its renewed strength and ghastly self-possession, made us shudder inwardly.

"'*Bonjour, Messieurs.*'

"His chin dropped on his breast. Tomassov addressed me in Russian.

"'It is he, the man himself . . .' I nodded and Tomassov went on in a tone of anguish: 'Yes, he! Brilliant, accomplished, envied by men, loved by that woman—this horror—this miserable thing that cannot die. Look at his eyes. It's terrible.'

"I did not look, but I understood what Tomassov meant. We could do nothing for him. This avenging winter of fate held both the fugitives and the pursuers in its iron grip. Compassion was but a vain word before that unrelenting destiny. I tried to say something about a convoy being no doubt collected in the village—

but I faltered at the mute glance Tomassov gave me. We knew what those convoys were like: appalling mobs of hopeless wretches driven on by the butts of Cossacks' lances, back to the frozen inferno, with their faces set away from their homes.

"Our two squadrons had been formed along the edge of the forest. The minutes of anguish were passing. The Frenchman suddenly struggled to his feet. We helped him almost without knowing what we were doing.

"'Come,' he said, in measured tones. 'This is the moment.' He paused for a long time, then with the same distinctness went on: 'On my word of honour, all faith is dead in me.'

"His voice lost suddenly its self-possession. After waiting a little while he added in a murmur: 'And even my courage. . . . Upon my honour.'

"Another long pause ensued before, with a great effort, he whispered hoarsely: 'Isn't this enough to move a heart of stone? Am I to go on my knees to you?'

"Again a deep silence fell upon the three of us. Then the French officer flung his last word of anger at Tomassov.

"'Milksop!'

"Not a feature of the poor fellow moved. I made up my mind to go and fetch a couple of our troopers to lead that miserable prisoner away to the village. There was nothing else for it. I had not moved six paces towards the group of horses and orderlies in front of our squadron when . . . but you have guessed it. Of course. And I, too, I guessed it, for I give you my word that the report of Tomassov's pistol was the most insignificant thing imaginable. The snow certainly does absorb sound. It was a mere feeble pop. Of the orderlies holding our horses I don't think one turned his head round.

"Yes. Tomassov had done it. Destiny had led that De Castel to the man who could understand him perfectly. But it was poor Tomassov's lot to be the predestined victim. You know what the world's justice and mankind's judgment are like. They fell heavily on him with a sort of inverted hypocrisy. Why! That brute of an adjutant, himself, was the first to set going horrified allusions to the shooting of a prisoner in cold blood! Tomassov was not dismissed from the service of course. But after the siege of Dantzig he asked for permission to resign from the army, and went away to bury himself in the depths of his province, where a vague story of some dark deed clung to him for years.

"Yes. He had done it. And what was it? One warrior's soul paying its debt a hundredfold to another warrior's soul by releasing it from a fate worse than death—the loss of all faith and courage. You may look on it in that way. I don't know. And perhaps poor Tomassov did not know himself. But I was the first to approach that appalling dark group on the snow: the Frenchman extended rigidly on his back, Tomassov kneeling on one knee rather nearer to the feet than to the Frenchman's head. He had taken his cap off and his hair shone like gold in the light drift of flakes that had begun to fall. He was stooping over the dead in a tenderly contemplative attitude. And his young, ingenuous face, with lowered eyelids, expressed no grief, no sternness, no horror—but was set in the repose of a profound, as if endless and endlessly silent, meditation."

PRINCE ROMAN

PRINCE ROMAN

"Events which happened seventy years ago are perhaps rather too far off to be dragged aptly into a mere conversation. Of course the year 1831 is for us an historical date, one of these fatal years when in the presence of the world's passive indignation and eloquent sympathies we had once more to murmur '*Væ Victis*' and count the cost in sorrow. Not that we were ever very good at calculating, either, in prosperity or in adversity. That's a lesson we could never learn, to the great exasperation of our enemies who have bestowed upon us the epithet of Incorrigible. . . ."

The speaker was of Polish nationality, that nationality not so much alive as surviving, which persists in thinking, breathing, speaking, hoping, and suffering in its grave, railed in by a million of bayonets and triple-sealed with the seals of three great empires.

The conversation was about aristocracy. How did this, nowadays discredited, subject come up? It is some years ago now and the precise recollection has faded. But I remember that it was not considered practically as an ingredient in the social mixture; and I verily believed that we arrived at that subject through some exchange of ideas about patriotism—a somewhat discredited sentiment, because the delicacy of our humanitarians regards it as a relic of barbarism. Yet neither the great Florentine painter who closed his eyes in death thinking of his city, nor St. Francis blessing with his last breath the town of Assisi, were barbarians. It requires a certain greatness of soul to interpret patriotism worthily—or else a sincerity of feeling denied to the vulgar refinement of modern thought which cannot understand the august simplicity of a sentiment proceeding from the very nature of things and men.

The aristocracy we were talking about was the very highest, the great families of Europe, not impoverished, not converted, not liberalized, the most distinctive and specialized class of all classes, for which even ambition itself does not exist among the usual incentives to activity and regulators of conduct.

The undisputed right of leadership having passed away from them, we judged that their great fortunes, their cosmopolitanism brought about by wide alliances, their elevated station, in which there is so little to gain and so much to lose, must make their position difficult in times of political commotion or national upheaval. No longer born to command—which is the very essence of aristocracy—it becomes difficult for them to do aught else but hold aloof from the great movements of popular passion.

We had reached that conclusion when the remark about far-off events was made and the date of 1831 mentioned. And the speaker continued:

"I don't mean to say that I knew Prince Roman at that remote time. I begin to feel pretty ancient, but I am not so ancient as that. In fact Prince Roman was married the very year my father was born. It was in 1828; the 19th Century was young yet and the Prince was even younger than the century, but I don't know exactly by how much. In any case his was an early marriage. It was an ideal alliance from every point of view. The girl was young and beautiful, an orphan heiress of a great name and of a great fortune. The Prince, then an officer in the Guards and distin-

guished amongst his fellows by something reserved and
reflective in his character, had fallen headlong in love
with her beauty, her charm, and the serious qualities of
her mind and heart. He was a rather silent young
man; but his glances, his bearing, his whole person expressed his absolute devotion to the woman of his
choice, a devotion which she returned in her own frank
and fascinating manner.

"The flame of this pure young passion promised to
burn for ever; and for a season it lit up the dry, cynical
atmosphere of the great world of St. Petersburg. The
Emperor Nicholas himself, the grandfather of the present
man, the one who died from the Crimean War, the last
perhaps of the Autocrats with a mystical belief in the
Divine character of his mission, showed some interest
in this pair of married lovers. It is true that Nicholas
kept a watchful eye on all the doings of the great
Polish nobles. The young people leading a life appro-
priate to their station were obviously wrapped up in
each other; and society, fascinated by the sincerity of a
feeling moving serenely among the artificialities of its
anxious and fastidious agitation, watched them with
benevolent indulgence and an amused tenderness.

"The marriage was the social event of 1828, in the
capital. Just forty years afterwards I was staying in
the country house of my mother's brother in our
southern provinces.

"It was the dead of winter. The great lawn in front
was as pure and smooth as an alpine snowfield, a white
and feathery level sparkling under the sun as if sprinkled
with diamond-dust, declining gently to the lake—a long,
sinuous piece of frozen water looking bluish and more
solid than the earth. A cold brilliant sun glided low
above an undulating horizon of great folds of snow in
which the villages of Ukrainian peasants remained out of

sight, like clusters of boats hidden in the hollows of a running sea. And everything was very still.

"I don't know now how I had managed to escape at eleven o'clock in the morning from the schoolroom. I was a boy of eight, the little girl, my cousin, a few months younger than myself, though hereditarily more quick-tempered, was less adventurous. So I had escaped alone; and presently I found myself in the great stone-paved hall, warmed by a monumental stove of white tiles, a much more pleasant locality than the schoolroom, which for some reason or other, perhaps hygienic, was always kept at a low temperature.

"We children were aware that there was a guest staying in the house. He had arrived the night before just as we were being driven off to bed. We broke back through the line of beaters to rush and flatten our noses against the dark window panes; but we were too late to see him alight. We had only watched in a ruddy glare the big travelling carriage on sleigh-runners harnessed with six horses, a black mass against the snow, going off to the stables, preceded by a horseman carrying a blazing ball of tow and resin in an iron basket at the end of a long stick swung from his saddle bow. Two stable boys had been sent out early in the afternoon along the snow-tracks to meet the expected guest at dusk and light his way with these road torches. At that time, you must remember, there was not a single mile of railways in our southern provinces. My little cousin and I had no knowledge of trains and engines, except from picture-books, as of things rather vague, extremely remote, and not particularly interesting unless to grownups who travelled abroad.

"Our notion of princes, perhaps a little more precise, was mainly literary and had a glamour reflected from

the light of fairy tales, in which princes always appear
young, charming, heroic, and fortunate. Yet, as well
as any other children, we could draw a firm line between
the real and the ideal. We knew that princes were
historical personages. And there was some glamour
in that fact, too. But what had driven me to roam
cautiously over the house like an escaped prisoner was
the hope of snatching an interview with a special friend
of mine, the head forester, who generally came to make
his report at that time of the day. I yearned for news
of a certain wolf. You know, in a country where wolves
are to be found, every winter almost brings forward an
individual eminent by the audacity of his misdeeds, by
his more perfect wolfishness—so to speak. I wanted
to hear some new thrilling tale of that wolf—perhaps the
dramatic story of his death. . . .

"But there was no one in the hall.

"Deceived in my hopes, I became suddenly very much
depressed. Unable to slip back in triumph to my
studies I elected to stroll spiritlessly into the billiard
room where certainly I had no business. There was
no one there either, and I felt very lost and desolate
under its high ceiling, all alone with the massive English
billiard table which seemed, in heavy, rectilinear silence,
to disapprove of that small boy's intrusion.

"As I began to think of retreat I heard footsteps in
the adjoining drawing room; and, before I could turn
tail and flee, my uncle and his guest appeared in the
doorway. To run away after having been seen would
have been highly improper, so I stood my ground.
My uncle looked surprised to see me; the guest by his
side was a spare man, of average stature, buttoned up
in a black frock coat and holding himself very erect
with a stiffly soldier-like carriage. From the folds of
a soft white cambric neck-cloth peeped the points of a

collar close against each shaven cheek. A few wisps of thin gray hair were brushed smoothly across the top of his bald head. His face, which must have been beautiful in its day, had preserved in age the harmonious simplicity of its lines. What amazed me was its even, almost deathlike pallor. He seemed to me to be prodigiously old. A faint smile, a mere momentary alteration in the set of his thin lips acknowledged my blushing confusion; and I became greatly interested to see him reach into the inside breastpocket of his coat. He extracted therefrom a lead pencil and a block of detachable pages, which he handed to my uncle with an almost imperceptible bow.

"I was very much astonished, but my uncle received it as a matter of course. He wrote something at which the other glanced and nodded slightly. A thin wrinkled hand—the hand was older than the face—patted my cheek and then rested on my head lightly. An unringing voice, a voice as colourless as the face itself, issued from his sunken lips, while the eyes, dark and still, looked down at me kindly.

"'And how old is this shy little boy?'"

"Before I could answer my uncle wrote down my age on the pad. I was deeply impressed. What was this ceremony? Was this personage too great to be spoken to? Again he glanced at the pad, and again gave a nod, and again that impersonal, mechanical voice was heard: 'He resembles his grandfather.'

"I remembered my paternal grandfather. He had died not long before. He, too, was prodigiously old. And to me it seemed perfectly natural that two such ancient and venerable persons should have known each other in the dim ages of creation before my birth. But my uncle obviously had not been aware of the fact. So obviously that the mechanical voice explained:

'Yes, yes. Comrades in '31. He was one of those who knew. Old times, my dear sir, old times. . . .'

"He made a gesture as if to put aside an importunate ghost. And now they were both looking down at me. I wondered whether anything was expected from me. To my round, questioning eyes my uncle remarked: 'He's completely deaf.' And the unrelated, inexpressive voice said: 'Give me your hand.'

"Acutely conscious of inky fingers I put it out timidly. I had never seen a deaf person before and was rather startled. He pressed it firmly and then gave me a final pat on the head.

"My uncle addressed me weightily: 'You have shaken hands with Prince Roman S——. It's something for you to remember when you grow up.'

"I was impressed by his tone. I had enough historical information to know vaguely that the Princes S—— counted amongst the sovereign Princes of Ruthenia till the union of all Ruthenian lands to the kingdom of Poland, when they became great Polish magnates, sometime at the beginning of the 15th Century. But what concerned me most was the failure of the fairy-tale glamour. It was shocking to discover a prince who was deaf, bald, meagre, and so prodigiously old. It never occurred to me that this imposing and disappointing man had been young, rich, beautiful; I could not know that he had been happy in the felicity of an ideal marriage uniting two young hearts, two great names and two great fortunes; happy with a happiness which, as in fairy tales, seemed destined to last for ever. . . .

"But it did not last for ever. It was fated not to last very long even by the measure of the days allotted to men's passage on this earth where enduring happiness is only found in the conclusion of fairy tales. A daughter was born to them and shortly afterwards, the health of the young princess began to fail. For a time she bore up with smiling intrepidity, sustained by the feeling that now her existence was necessary for the happiness of two lives. But at last the husband, thoroughly alarmed by the rapid changes in her appearance, obtained an unlimited leave and took her away from the capital to his parents in the country.

"The old prince and princess were extremely frightened at the state of their beloved daughter-in-law. Preparations were at once made for a journey abroad. But it seemed as if it were already too late; and the invalid herself opposed the project with gentle obstinacy. Thin and pale in the great armchair, where the insidious and obscure nervous malady made her appear smaller and more frail every day without effacing the smile of her eyes or the charming grace of her wasted face, she clung to her native land and wished to breathe her native air. Nowhere else could she expect to get well so quickly, nowhere else would it be so easy for her to die.

"She died before her little girl was two years old. The grief of the husband was terrible and the more alarming to his parents because perfectly silent and dry-eyed. After the funeral, while the immense bareheaded crowd of peasants surrounding the private chapel on the grounds was dispersing, the Prince, waving away his friends and relations, remained alone to watch the masons of the estate closing the family vault. When the last stone was in position he uttered a groan, the first sound of pain which had escaped from him for days, and walking away with lowered head shut himself up again in his apartments.

"His father and mother feared for his reason. His

outward tranquillity was appalling to them. They had nothing to trust to but that very youth which made his despair so self-absorbed and so intense. Old Prince John, fretful and anxious, repeated: 'Poor Roman should be roused somehow. He's so young.' But they could find nothing to rouse him with. And the old princess, wiping her eyes, wished in her heart he were young enough to come and cry at her knee.

"In time Prince Roman, making an effort, would join now and again the family circle. But it was as if his heart and his mind had been buried in the family vault with the wife he had lost. He took to wandering in the woods with a gun, watched over secretly by one of the keepers, who would report in the evening that 'His Serenity has never fired a shot all day.' Sometimes walking to the stables in the morning he would order in subdued tones a horse to be saddled, wait switching his boot till it was led up to him, then mount without a word and ride out of the gates at a walking pace. He would be gone all day. People saw him on the roads looking neither to the right nor to the left, white-faced, sitting rigidly in the saddle like a horseman of stone on a living mount.

"The peasants working in the fields, the great unhedged fields, looked after him from the distance; and sometimes some sympathetic old woman on the threshold of a low, thatched hut was moved to make the sign of the cross in the air behind his back; as though he were one of themselves, a simple village soul struck by a sore affliction.

"He rode looking straight ahead, seeing no one, as if the earth were empty and all mankind buried in that grave which had opened so suddenly in his path to swallow up his happiness. What were men to him with their sorrows, joys, labours and passions from which she who had been all the world to him had been cut off so early?

"They did not exist; and he would have felt as completely lonely and abandoned as a man in the toils of a cruel nightmare if it had not been for this countryside where he had been born and had spent his happy boyish years. He knew it well—every slight rise crowned with trees amongst the ploughed fields, every dell concealing a village. The dammed streams made a chain of lakes set in the green meadows. Far away to the north the great Lithuanian forest faced the sun, no higher than a hedge; and to the south, the way to the plains, the vast brown spaces of the earth touched the blue sky.

"And this familiar landscape associated with the days without thought and without sorrow, this land the charm of which he felt without even looking at it soothed his pain, like the presence of an old friend who sits silent and disregarded by one in some dark hour of life.

"One afternoon, it happened that the Prince after turning his horse's head for home remarked a low dense cloud of dark dust cutting off slantwise a part of the view. He reined in on a knoll and peered. There were slender gleams of steel here and there in that cloud, and it contained moving forms which revealed themselves at last as a long line of peasant carts full of soldiers, moving slowly in double file under the escort of mounted Cossacks.

"It was like an immense reptile creeping over the fields; its head dipped out of sight in a slight hollow and its tail went on writhing and growing shorter as though the monster were eating its way slowly into the very heart of the land.

"The Prince directed his way through a village lying a little off the track. The roadside inn with its stable,

byre, and barn under one enormous thatched roof
resembled a deformed, hunch-backed, ragged giant,
sprawling amongst the small huts of the peasants.
The innkeeper, a portly, dignified Jew, clad in a black
satin coat reaching down to his heels and girt with a
red sash, stood at the door stroking his long silvery
beard.

"He watched the Prince approach and bowed gravely
from the waist, not expecting to be noticed even, since
it was well known that their young lord had no eyes for
anything or anybody in his grief. It was quite a shock
for him when the Prince pulled up and asked:

"'What's all this, Yankel?'

"'That is, please your Serenity, that is a convoy of
footsoldiers they are hurrying down to the south.'

"He glanced right and left cautiously, but as there was
no one near but some children playing in the dust of
the village street, he came up close to the stirrup.

"'Doesn't your Serenity know? It has begun already
down there. All the landowners great and small are
out in arms and even the common people have risen.
Only yesterday the saddler from Grodek (it was a tiny
market-town near by) went through here with his two
apprentices on his way to join. He left even his cart
with me. I gave him a guide through our neighbourhood. You know, your Serenity, our people they
travel a lot and they see all that's going on, and they
know all the roads.'

"He tried to keep down his excitement, for the Jew
Yankel, innkeeper and tenant of all the mills on the
estate, was a Polish patriot. And in a still lower voice:

"'I was already a married man when the French and
all the other nations passed this way with Napoleon.
Tse! Tse! That was a great harvest for death, nu!
Perhaps this time God will help.'

"The Prince nodded. 'Perhaps'—and falling into deep meditation he let his horse take him home.

"That night he wrote a letter, and early in the morning sent a mounted express to the post town. During the day he came out of his taciturnity, to the great joy of the family circle, and conversed with his father of recent events—the revolt in Warsaw, the flight of the Grand Duke Constantine, the first slight successes of the Polish army (at that time there was a Polish army); the risings in the provinces. Old Prince John, moved and uneasy, speaking from a purely aristocratic point of view, mistrusted the popular origins of the movement, regretted its democratic tendencies, and did not believe in the possibility of success. He was sad, inwardly agitated.

"'I am judging all this calmly. There are secular principles of legitimity and order which have been violated in this reckless enterprise for the sake of most subversive illusions. Though of course the patriotic impulses of the heart . . .'

"Prince Roman had listened in a thoughtful attitude. He took advantage of the pause to tell his father quietly that he had sent that morning a letter to St. Petersburg resigning his commission in the Guards.

"The old prince remained silent. He thought that he ought to have been consulted. His son was also ordnance officer to the Emperor and he knew that the Tsar would never forget this appearance of defection in a Polish noble. In a discontented tone he pointed out to his son that as it was he had an unlimited leave. The right thing would have been to keep quiet. They had too much tact at Court to recall a man of his name. Or at worst some distant mission might have been asked for—to the Caucasus for instance—away from this unhappy struggle which was wrong in principle and therefore destined to fail.

"'Presently you shall find yourself without any interest in life and with no occupation. And you shall need something to occupy you, my poor boy. You have acted rashly, I fear.'

"Prince Roman murmured.

"'I thought it better.'

"His father faltered under his steady gaze.

"'Well, well—perhaps! But as ordnance officer to the Emperor and in favour with all the Imperial family . . .'

"'Those people had never been heard of when our house was already illustrious,' the young man let fall disdainfully.

"This was the sort of remark to which the old prince was sensible.

"'Well—perhaps it is better,' he conceded at last.

"The father and son parted affectionately for the night. The next day Prince Roman seemed to have fallen back into the depths of his indifference. He rode out as usual. He remembered that the day before he had seen a reptile-like convoy of soldiery, bristling with bayonets, crawling over the face of that land which was his. The woman he loved had been his, too. Death had robbed him of her. Her loss had been to him a moral shock. It had opened his heart to a greater sorrow, his mind to a vaster thought, his eyes to all the past and to the existence of another love fraught with pain but as mysteriously imperative as that lost one to which he had entrusted his happiness.

"That evening he retired earlier than usual and rang for his personal servant.

"'Go and see if there is light yet in the quarters of the Master-of-the-Horse. If he is still up ask him to come and speak to me.'

"While the servant was absent on this errand the

Prince tore up hastily some papers, locked the drawers of his desk, and hung a medallion, containing the miniature of his wife, round his neck against his breast.

"The man the Prince was expecting belonged to that past which the death of his love had called to life. He was of a family of small nobles who for generations had been adherents, servants, and friends of the Princes S——. He remembered the times before the last partition and had taken part in the struggles of the last hour. He was a typical old Pole of that class, with a great capacity for emotion, for blind enthusiasm; with martial instincts and simple beliefs; and even with the old-time habit of larding his speech with Latin words. And his kindly shrewd eyes, his ruddy face, his lofty brow and his thick, gray, pendent moustache were also very typical of his kind.

"'Listen, Master Francis,' the Prince said familiarly and without preliminaries. 'Listen, old friend. I am going to vanish from here quietly. I go where something louder than my grief and yet something with a voice very like it calls me. I confide in you alone. You will say what's necessary when the time comes.'

"The old man understood. His extended hands trembled exceedingly. But as soon as he found his voice he thanked God aloud for letting him live long enough to see the descendant of the illustrious family in its youngest generation give an example *coram Gentibus* of the love of his country and of valour in the field. He doubted not of his dear Prince attaining a place in council and in war worthy of his high birth; he saw already that *in fulgore* of family glory *affulget patride serenitas*. At the end of the speech he burst into tears and fell into the Prince's arms.

"The Prince quieted the old man and when he had

him seated in an armchair and comparatively composed he said:

"'Don't misunderstand me, Master Francis. You know how I loved my wife. A loss like that opens one's eyes to unsuspected truths. There is no question here of leadership and glory. I mean to go alone and to fight obscurely in the ranks. I am going to offer my country what is mine to offer, that is my life, as simply as the saddler from Grodek who went through yesterday with his apprentices.'

"The old man cried out at this. That could never be. He could not allow it. But he had to give way before the arguments and the express will of the Prince.

"'Ha! If you say that it is a matter of feeling and conscience— so be it. But you cannot go utterly alone. Alas! that I am too old to be of any use. *Cripit verba dolor*, my dear Prince, at the thought that I am over seventy and of no more account in the world than a cripple in the church porch. It seems that to sit at home and pray to God for the nation and for you is all I am fit for. But there is my son, my youngest son, Peter. He will make a worthy companion for you. And as it happens he's staying with me here. There has not been for ages a Prince S——— hazarding his life without a companion of our name to ride by his side. You must have by you somebody who knows who you are if only to let your parents and your old servant hear what is happening to you. And when does your Princely Mightiness mean to start?'

"'In an hour,' said the Prince; and the old man hurried off to warn his son.

"Prince Roman took up a candlestick and walked quietly along a dark corridor in the silent house. The head-nurse said afterwards that waking up suddenly she saw the Prince looking at his child, one hand shading the light from its eyes. He stood and gazed at her for some time, and then putting the candlestick on the floor bent over the cot and kissed lightly the little girl who did not wake. He went out noiselessly, taking the light away with him. She saw his face perfectly well, but she could read nothing of his purpose in it. It was pale but perfectly calm and after he turned away from the cot he never looked back at it once.

"The only other trusted person, besides the old man and his son Peter, was the Jew Yankel. When he asked the Prince where precisely he wanted to be guided the Prince answered: 'To the nearest party.' A grandson of the Jew, a lanky youth, conducted the two young men by little-known paths across woods and morasses, and led them in sight of the few fires of a small detachment camped in a hollow. Some invisible horses neighed, a voice in the dark cried: 'Who goes there?' . . . and the young Jew departed hurriedly, explaining that he must make haste home to be in time for keeping the Sabbath.

"Thus humbly and in accord with the simplicity of the vision of duty he saw when death had removed the brilliant bandage of happiness from his eyes, did Prince Roman bring his offering to his country. His companion made himself known as the son of the Master-of-the-Horse to the Princes S——— and declared him to be a relation, a distant cousin from the same parts as himself and, as people presumed, of the same name. In truth no one inquired much. Two more young men clearly of the right sort had joined. Nothing more natural.

"Prince Roman did not remain long in the south. One day while scouting with several others, they were ambushed near the entrance of a village by some Russian infantry. The first discharge laid low a good

many and the rest scattered in all directions. The
Russians, too, did not stay, being afraid of a return in
force. After some time, the peasants coming to view
the scene extricated Prince Roman from under his
dead horse. He was unhurt but his faithful companion
had been one of the first to fall. The Prince helped the
peasants to bury him and the other dead.

"Then alone, not certain where to find the body of
partizans which was constantly moving about in all
directions, he resolved to try and join the main Polish
army facing the Russians on the borders of Lithuania.
Disguised in peasant clothes, in case of meeting some
marauding Cossacks, he wandered a couple of weeks
before he came upon a village occupied by a regiment
of Polish cavalry on outpost duty.

"On a bench, before a peasant hut of a better sort,
sat an elderly officer whom he took for the colonel.
The Prince approached respectfully, told his story
shortly and stated his desire to enlist; and when asked
his name by the officer, who had been looking him over
carefully, he gave on the spur of the moment the name
of his dead companion.

"The elderly officer thought to himself: Here's the
son of some peasant proprietor of the liberated class.
He liked his appearance.

"'And can you read and write, my good fellow?' he
asked.

"'Yes, your honour, I can,' said the Prince.

"'Good. Come along inside the hut; the regimental
adjutant is there. He will enter your name and ad-
minister the oath to you.'

"The adjutant stared very hard at the newcomer
but said nothing. When all the forms had been gone
through and the recruit gone out, he turned to his superior officer.

"'Do you know who that is?'

"'Who? That Peter? A likely chap.'

"'That's Prince Roman S——.'

"'Nonsense.'

"But the adjutant was positive. He had seen the Prince several times, about two years before, in the Castle in Warsaw. He had even spoken to him once at a reception of officers held by the Grand Duke.

"'He's changed. He seems much older, but I am certain of my man. I have a good memory for faces.'

"The two officers looked at each other in silence.

"'He's sure to be recognized sooner or later,' murmured the adjutant. The colonel shrugged his shoulders.

"'It's no affair of ours—if he has a fancy to serve in the ranks. As to being recognized it's not so likely. All our officers and men come from the other end of Poland.'

"He meditated gravely for a while, then smiled. 'He told me he could read and write. There's nothing to prevent me making him a sergeant at the first opportunity. He's sure to shape all right.'

"Prince Roman as a non-commissioned officer surpassed the colonel's expectations. Before long Sergeant Peter became famous for his resourcefulness and courage. It was not the reckless courage of a desperate man; it was a self-possessed, as if conscientious, valour which nothing could dismay; a boundless but equable devotion, unaffected by time, by reverses, by the discouragement of endless retreats, by the bitterness of waning hopes and the horrors of pestilence added to the toils and perils of war. It was in this year that the cholera made its first appearance in Europe. It devastated the camps of both armies, affecting the firmest minds with the terror of a mysterious death stalking silently between the piled-up arms and around the bivouac fires.

"A sudden shriek would wake up the harassed soldiers and they would see in the glow of embers one of themselves writhe on the ground like a worm trodden on by an invisible foot. And before the dawn broke he would be stiff and cold. Parties so visited have been known to rise like one man, abandon the fire and run off into the night in mute panic. Or a comrade talking to you on the march would stammer suddenly in the middle of a sentence, roll affrighted eyes, and fall down with distorted face and blue lips, breaking the ranks with the convulsions of his agony. Men were struck in the saddle, on sentry duty, in the firing line, carrying orders, serving the guns. I have been told that in a battalion forming under fire with perfect steadiness for the assault of a village, three cases occurred within five minutes at the head of the column; and the attack could not be delivered because the leading companies scattered all over the fields like chaff before the wind

"Sergeant Peter, young as he was, had a great influence over his men. It was said that the number of desertions in the squadron in which he served was less than in any other in the whole of that cavalry division. Such was supposed to be the compelling example of one man's quiet intrepidity in facing every form of danger and terror.

"However that may be, he was liked and trusted generally. When the end came and the remnants of that army corps, hard pressed on all sides, were preparing to cross the Prussian frontier, Sergeant Peter had enough influence to rally round him a score of troopers. He managed to escape with them at night, from the hemmed-in army. He led this band through 200 miles of country covered by numerous Russian detachments and ravaged by the cholera. But this was not to avoid captivity, to go into hiding and try to save themselves. No. He led them into a fortress which was still occupied by the Poles, and where the last stand of the vanquished revolution was to be made.

"This looks like mere fanaticism. But fanaticism is human. Man has adored ferocious divinities. There is ferocity in every passion, even in love itself. The religion of undying hope resembles the mad cult of despair, of death, of annihilation. The difference lies in the moral motive springing from the secret needs and the unexpressed aspiration of the believers. It is only to vain men that all is vanity; and all is deception only to those who have never been sincere with themselves.

"It was in the fortress that my grandfather found himself together with Sergeant Peter. My grandfather was a neighbour of the S———— family in the country but he did not know Prince Roman, who however knew his name perfectly well. The Prince introduced himself one night as they both sat on the ramparts, leaning against a gun carriage.

"The service he wished to ask for was, in case of his being killed, to have the intelligence conveyed to his parents.

"They talked in low tones, the other servants of the piece lying about near them. My grandfather gave the required promise, and then asked frankly—for he was greatly interested by the disclosure so unexpectedly made:

"'But tell me, Prince, why this request? Have you any evil forebodings as to yourself?'

"'Not in the least; I was thinking of my people. They have no idea where I am,' answered Prince Roman. 'I'll engage to do as much for you, if you like. It's certain that half of us at least shall be killed before

the end, so there's an even chance of one of us surviving
the other.'

"My grandfather told him where, as he supposed,
his wife and children were then. From that moment
till the end of the siege the two were much together.
On the day of the great assault my grandfather received a severe wound. The town was taken. Next
day the citadel itself, its hospital full of dead and dying,
its magazines empty, its defenders having burnt their
last cartridge, opened its gates.

"During all the campaign the Prince, exposing his
person conscientiously on every occasion, had not
received a scratch. No one had recognized him or at
any rate had betrayed his identity. Till then, as long
as he did his duty, it had mattered nothing who he was.

"Now, however, the position was changed. As ex-
guardsman and as late ordnance officer to the Emperor,
this rebel ran a serious risk of being given special attention in the shape of a firing squad at ten paces.
For more than a month he remained lost in the miserable crowd of prisoners packed in the casemates of the
citadel, with just enough food to keep body and soul
together but otherwise allowed to die from wounds,
privation, and disease at the rate of forty or so a day.

"The position of the fortress being central, new parties, captured in the open in the course of a thorough
pacification, were being sent in frequently. Amongst
such newcomers there happened to be a young man, a
personal friend of the Prince from his school days. He
recognized him, and in the extremity of his dismay
cried aloud: 'My God! Roman, you here!'

"It is said that years of life embittered by remorse
paid for this momentary lack of self-control. All this
happened in the main quadrangle of the citadel. The
warning gesture of the Prince came too late. An officer

c

of the gendarmes on guard had heard the exclamation. The incident appeared to him worth inquiring into. The investigation which followed was not very arduous because the Prince, asked categorically for his real name, owned up at once.

"The intelligence of the Prince S—— being found amongst the prisoners was sent to St. Petersburg. His parents were already there living in sorrow, incertitude, and apprehension. The capital of the Empire was the safest place to reside in for a noble whose son had disappeared so mysteriously from home in a time of rebellion. The old people had not heard from him, or of him, for months. They took care not to contradict the rumours of suicide from despair circulating in the great world, which remembered the interesting love-match, the charming and frank happiness brought to an end by death. But they hoped secretly that their son survived, and that he had been able to cross the frontier with that part of the army which had surrendered to the Prussians.

"The news of his captivity was a crushing blow. Directly, nothing could be done for him. But the greatness of their name, of their position, their wide relations and connections in the highest spheres, enabled his parents to act indirectly and they moved heaven and earth, as the saying is, to save their son from the 'consequences of his madness,' as poor Prince John did not hesitate to express himself. Great personages were approached by society leaders, high dignitaries were interviewed, powerful officials were induced to take an interest in that affair. The help of every possible secret influence was enlisted. Some private secretaries got heavy bribes. The mistress of a certain senator obtained a large sum of money.

"But, as I have said, in such a glaring case no direct

appeal could be made and no open steps taken. All that could be done was to incline by private representation the mind of the President of the Military Commission to the side of clemency. He ended by being impressed by the hints and suggestions, some of them from very high quarters, which he received from St. Petersburg. And, after all, the gratitude of such great nobles as the Princes S—— was something worth having from a worldly point of view. He was a good Russian but he was also a good-natured man. Moreover, the hate of Poles was not at that time a cardinal article of patriotic creed as it became some thirty years later. He felt well disposed at first sight towards that young man, bronzed, thin-faced, worn out by months of hard campaigning, the hardships of the siege and the rigours of captivity.

"The Commission was composed of three officers. It sat in the citadel in a bare vaulted room behind a long black table. Some clerks occupied the two ends, and besides the gendarmes who brought in the Prince there was no one else there.

"Within those four sinister walls shutting out from him all the sights and sounds of liberty, all hopes of the future, all consoling illusions—alone in the face of his enemies erected for judges, who can tell how much love of life there was in Prince Roman? How much remained in that sense of duty, revealed to him in sorrow? How much of his awakened love for his native country? That country which demands to be loved as no other country has ever been loved, with the mournful affection one bears to the unforgotten dead and with the inextinguishable fire of a hopeless passion which only a living, breathing, warm ideal can kindle in our breasts for our pride, for our weariness, for our exultation, for our undoing.

"There is something monstrous in the thought of such an exaction till it stands before us embodied in the shape of a fidelity without fear and without reproach. Nearing the supreme moment of his life the Prince could only have had the feeling that it was about to end. He answered the questions put to him clearly, concisely —with the most profound indifference. After all those tense months of action, to talk was a weariness to him. But he concealed it, lest his foes should suspect in his manner the apathy of discouragement or the numbness of a crushed spirit. The details of his conduct could have no importance one way or another; with his thoughts these men had nothing to do. He preserved a scrupulously courteous tone. He had refused the permission to sit down.

"What happened at this preliminary examination is only known from the presiding officer. Pursuing the only possible course in that glaringly bad case he tried from the first to bring to the Prince's mind the line of defence he wished him to take. He absolutely framed his questions so as to put the right answers in the culprit's mouth, going so far as to suggest the very words how, distracted by excessive grief after his young wife' death, rendered irresponsible for his conduct by his despair, in a moment of blind recklessness, without realizing the highly reprehensible nature of the act, nor yet its danger and its dishonour, he went off to join the nearest rebels on a sudden impulse. And that now penitently . . .

"But Prince Roman was silent. The military judge looked at him hopefully. In silence he reached for pen and wrote on a sheet of paper he found under his hand: 'I joined the national rising from conviction.'

"He pushed the paper across the table. The president took it up, showed it in turn to his two colleagues sitting to the right and left, then looking fixedly at Prince Roman let it fall from his hand. And the silence remained unbroken till he spoke to the gendarmes ordering them to remove the prisoner.

"Such was the written testimony of Prince Roman in the supreme moment of his life. I have heard that the Princes of the S——— family, in all its branches, adopted the last two words: 'From conviction' for the device under the armorial bearings of their house. I don't know whether the report is true. My uncle could not tell me. He remarked only, that naturally, it was not to be seen on Prince Roman's own seal.

"He was condemned for life to Siberian mines. Emperor Nicholas, who always took personal cognizance of all sentences on Polish nobility, wrote with his own hand in the margin: 'The authorities are severely warned to take care that this convict walks in chains like any other criminal every step of the way.'

"It was a sentence of deferred death. Very few survived entombment in these mines for more than three years. Yet as he was reported as still alive at the end of that time he was allowed, on a petition of his parents and by way of exceptional grace, to serve as common soldier in the Caucasus. All communication with him was forbidden. He had no civil rights. For all practical purposes except that of suffering he was a dead man. The little child he had been so careful not to wake up when he kissed her in her cot, inherited all the fortune after Prince John's death. Her existence saved those immense estates from confiscation.

"It was twenty-five years before Prince Roman, stone deaf, his health broken, was permitted to return to Poland. His daughter married splendidly to a Polish Austrian *grand seigneur* and, moving in the cosmopolitan sphere of the highest European aristocracy, lived mostly abroad in Nice and Vienna. He, settling down on one of her estates, not the one with the palatial residence but another where there was a modest little house, saw very little of her.

"But Prince Roman did not shut himself up as if his work were done. There was hardly anything done in the private and public life of the neighbourhood, in which Prince Roman's advice and assistance were not called upon, and never in vain. It was well said that his days did not belong to himself but to his fellow citizens. And especially he was the particular friend of all returned exiles, helping them with purse and advice, arranging their affairs and finding them means of livelihood.

"I heard from my uncle many tales of his devoted activity, in which he was always guided by a simple wisdom, a high sense of honour, and the most scrupulous conception of private and public probity. He remains a living figure for me because of that meeting in a billiard room, when, in my anxiety to hear about a particularly wolfish wolf, I came in momentary contact with a man who was preëminently a man amongst all men capable of feeling deeply, of believing steadily, of loving ardently.

"I remember to this day the grasp of Prince Roman's bony, wrinkled hand closing on my small inky paw, and my uncle's half-serious, half-amused way of looking down at his trespassing nephew.

"They moved on and forgot that little boy. But I did not move; I gazed after them, not so much disappointed as disconcerted by this prince so utterly unlike a prince in a fairy tale. They moved very slowly across the room. Before reaching the other door the Prince stopped, and I heard him—I seem to hear him now—saying: 'I wish you would write to

Vienna about filling up that post. He's a most deserving fellow—and your recommendation would be decisive.'

"My uncle's face turned to him expressed genuine wonder. It said as plainly as any speech could say: What better recommendation than a father's can be needed? The Prince was quick at reading expressions. Again he spoke with the toneless accent of a man who has not heard his own voice for years, for whom the soundless world is like an abode of silent shades.

"And to this day I remember the very words: 'I ask you because, you see, my daughter and my son-in-law don't believe me to be a good judge of men. They think that I let myself be guided too much by mere sentiment.'"

THE TALE

THE TALE

OUTSIDE the large single window the crepuscular light was dying out slowly in a great square gleam without colour, framed rigidly in the gathering shades of the room.

It was a long room. The irresistible tide of the night ran into the most distant part of it, where the whispering of a man's voice, passionately interrupted and passionately renewed, seemed to plead against the answering murmurs of infinite sadness.

At last no answering murmur came. His movement when he rose slowly from his knees by the side of the deep, shadowy couch holding the shadowy suggestion of a reclining woman revealed him tall under the low ceiling, and sombre all over except for the crude discord of the white collar under the shape of his head and the faint, minute spark of a brass button here and there on his uniform.

He stood over her a moment, masculine and mysterious in his immobility, before he sat down on a chair near by. He could see only the faint oval of her upturned face and, extended on her black dress, her pale hands, a moment before abandoned to his kisses and now as if too weary to move.

He dared not make a sound, shrinking as a man would do from the prosaic necessities of existence. As usual, it was the woman who had the courage. Her voice was heard first—almost conventional while her being vibrated yet with conflicting emotions.

"Tell me something," she said.

The darkness hid his surprise and then his smile. Had he not just said to her everything worth saying in the world—and that not for the first time!

"What am I to tell you?" he asked, in a voice creditably steady. He was beginning to feel grateful to her for that something final in her tone which had eased the strain.

"Why not tell me a tale?"

"A tale!" He was really amazed.

"Yes. Why not?"

These words came with a slight petulance, the hint of a loved woman's capricious will, which is capricious only because it feels itself to be a law, embarrassing sometimes and always difficult to elude.

"Why not?" he repeated, with a slightly mocking accent, as though he had been asked to give her the moon. But now he was feeling a little angry with her for that feminine mobility that slips out of an emotion as easily as out of a splendid gown.

He heard her say, a little unsteadily with a sort of fluttering intonation which made him think suddenly of a butterfly's flight:

"You used to tell—your—your simple and—and professional—tales very well at one time. Or well enough to interest me. You had a—a sort of art—in the days—the days before the war."

"Really?" he said, with involuntary gloom. "But now, you see, the war is going on," he continued in such a dead, equable tone that she felt a slight chill fall over her shoulders. And yet she persisted. For there's nothing more unswerving in the world than a woman's caprice.

"It could be a tale not of this world," she explained.

"You want a tale of the other, the better world?" he asked, with a matter-of-fact surprise. "You must evoke for that task those who have already gone there."

"No. I don't mean that. I mean another—some other—world. In the universe—not in heaven."

"I am relieved. But you forget that I have only five days' leave."

"Yes. And I've also taken a five days' leave from—from my duties."

"I like that word."

"What word?"

"Duty."

"It is horrible—sometimes."

"Oh, that's because you think it's narrow. But it isn't. It contains infinities, and—and so——"

"What is this jargon?"

He disregarded the interjected scorn. "An infinity of absolution, for instance," he continued. "But as to this 'another world'—who's going to look for it and for the tale that is in it?"

"You," she said, with a strange, almost rough, sweet-ness of assertion.

He made a shadowy movement of assent in his chair, the irony of which not even the gathered darkness could render mysterious.

"As you will. In that world, then, there was once upon a time a Commanding Officer and a Northman. Put in the capitals, please, because they had no other names. It was a world of seas and continents and islands——"

"Like the earth," she murmured, bitterly.

"Yes. What else could you expect from sending a man made of our common, tormented clay on a voyage of discovery? What else could he find? What else could you understand or care for, or feel the existence of even? There was comedy in it, and slaughter."

"Always like the earth," she murmured.

"Always. And since I could find in the universe only what was deeply rooted in the fibres of my being there was love in it, too. But we won't talk of that."

"No. We won't," she said, in a neutral tone which concealed perfectly her relief—or her disappointment. Then after a pause she added: "It's going to be a comic story."

"Well——" he paused, too. "Yes. In a way. In a very grim way. It will be human, and, as you know, comedy is but a matter of the visual angle. And it won't be a noisy story. All the long guns in it will be dumb—as dumb as so many telescopes."

"Ah, there are guns in it, then! And may I ask—where?"

"Afloat. You remember that the world of which we speak had its seas. A war was going on in it. It was a funny world and terribly in earnest. Its war was being carried on over the land, over the water, under the water, up in the air, and even under the ground. And many young men in it, mostly in wardrooms and mess-rooms, used to say to each other—pardon the unparliamentary word—they used to say, 'It's a damned bad war, but it's better than no war at all.' Sounds flippant, doesn't it?"

He heard a nervous, impatient sigh in the depths of the couch while he went on without a pause.

"And yet there is more in it than meets the eye. I mean more wisdom. Flippancy, like comedy, is but a matter of visual first-impression. That world was not very wise. But there was in it a certain amount of common working sagacity. That, however, was mostly worked by the neutrals in diverse ways, public and private, which had to be watched; watched by acute minds

and also by actual sharp eyes. They had to be very
sharp indeed, too, I assure you."

"I can imagine," she murmured, appreciatively.

"What is there that you can't imagine?" he pronounced, soberly. "You have the world in you. But
let us go back to our commanding officer, who, of
course, commanded a ship of a sort. My tales if often
professional (as you remarked just now) have never
been technical. So I'll just tell you that the ship was of
a very ornamental sort once, with lots of grace and ele-
gance and luxury about her. Yes, once! She was like
a pretty woman who had suddenly put on a suit of
sackcloth and stuck revolvers in her belt. But she
floated lightly, she moved nimbly, she was quite good
enough."

"That was the opinion of the commanding officer?"
said the voice from the couch.

"It was. He used to be sent out with her along certain coasts to see—what he could see. Just that.
And sometimes he had some preliminary information to
help him, and sometimes he had not. And it was all
one, really. It was about as useful as information
trying to convey the locality and intentions of a cloud,
of a phantom taking shape here and there and impossible to seize, would have been.

"It was in the early days of the war. What at first
used to amaze the commanding officer was the unchanged face of the waters, with its familiar expression,
neither more friendly nor more hostile. On fine days
the sun strikes sparks upon the blue; here and there a
peaceful smudge of smoke hangs in the distance, and it
is impossible to believe that the familiar clear horizon
traces the limit of one great circular ambush.

"Yes, it is impossible to believe, till some day you see
a ship not your own ship (that isn't so impressive),

but some ship in company, blow up all of a sudden and plop under almost before you know what has happened to her. Then you begin to believe. Henceforth you go out for the work to see—what you can see, and you keep on at it with the conviction that some day you will die from something you have not seen. One envies the soldiers at the end of the day, wiping the sweat and blood from their faces, counting the dead fallen to their hands, looking at the devastated fields, the torn earth that seems to suffer and bleed with them. One does, really. The final brutality of it—the taste of primitive passion—the ferocious frankness of the blow struck with one's hand—the direct call and the straight response. Well, the sea gave you nothing of that, and seemed to pretend that there was nothing the matter with the world."

She interrupted, stirring a little.

"Oh, yes. Sincerity — frankness — passion — three words of your gospel. Don't I know them!"

"Think! Isn't it ours—believed in common?" he asked, anxiously, yet without expecting an answer, and went on at once: "Such were the feelings of the commanding officer. When the night came trailing over the sea, hiding what looked like the hypocrisy of an old friend, it was a relief. The night blinds you frankly—and there are circumstances when the sunlight may grow as odious to one as falsehood itself. Night is all right.

"At night the commanding officer could let his thoughts get away—I won't tell you where. Somewhere where there was no choice but between truth and death. But thick weather, though it blinded one, brought no such relief. Mist is deceitful, the dead luminosity of the fog is irritating. It seems that you *ought* to see.

"One gloomy, nasty day the ship was steaming along her beat in sight of a rocky, dangerous coast that stood out intensely black like an India-ink drawing on gray paper. Presently the second in command spoke to his chief. He thought he saw something on the water, to seaward. Small wreckage, perhaps.

"'But there shouldn't be any wreckage here, sir,' he remarked.

"'No,' said the commanding officer. 'The last reported submarined ships were sunk a long way to the westward. But one never knows. There may have been others since then not reported nor seen. Gone with all hands.'

"That was how it began. The ship's course was altered to pass the object close; for it was necessary to have a good look at what one could see. Close, but without touching; for it was not advisable to come in contact with objects of any form whatever floating casually about. Close, but without stopping or even diminishing speed; for in those times it was not prudent to linger on any particular spot, even for a moment. I may tell you at once that the object was not dangerous in itself. No use in describing it. It may have been nothing more remarkable than, say, a barrel of a certain shape and colour. But it was significant.

"The smooth bow-wave hove it up as if for a closer inspection, and then the ship, brought again to her course, turned her back on it with indifference, while twenty pairs of eyes on her deck stared in all directions trying to see—what they could see.

"The commanding officer and his second in command discussed the object with understanding. It appeared to them to be not so much a proof of the sagacity as of the activity of certain neutrals. This activity had in many cases taken the form of replenish-

ing the stores of certain submarines at sea. This was
generally believed, if not absolutely known. But the
very nature of things in those early days pointed that
way. The object, looked at closely and turned away
from with apparent indifference, put it beyond doubt
that something of the sort had been done somewhere
in the neighbourhood.

"The object in itself was more than suspect. But
the fact of its being left in evidence roused other suspicions. Was it the result of some deep and devilish purpose? As to that all speculation soon appeared to be a
vain thing. Finally the two officers came to the conclusion that it was left there most likely by accident,
complicated possibly by some unforeseen necessity;
such, perhaps, as the sudden need to get away quickly
from the spot, or something of that kind.

"Their discussion had been carried on in curt, weighty
phrases, separated by long, thoughtful silences. And
all the time their eyes roamed about the horizon in
an everlasting, almost mechanical effort of vigilance.
The younger man summed up grimly:

"'Well, it's evidence. That's what this is. Evidence of what we were pretty certain of before. And
plain, too.'

"'And much good it will do to us,' retorted the
commanding officer. 'The parties are miles away; the
submarine, devil only knows where, ready to kill;
and the noble neutral slipping away to the eastward,
ready to lie!'

"The second in command laughed a little at the tone.
But he guessed that the neutral wouldn't even have to
lie very much. Fellows like that, unless caught in the
very act, felt themselves pretty safe. They could
afford to chuckle. That fellow was probably chuckling
to himself. It's very possible he had been before at the

game and didn't care a rap for the bit of evidence left
behind. It was a game in which practice made one
bold and successful, too.

"And again he laughed faintly. But his commanding
officer was in revolt against the murderous stealthiness
of methods and the atrocious callousness of complicities
that seemed to taint the very source of men's deep
emotions and noblest activities; to corrupt their
imagination which builds up the final conceptions of
life and death. He suffered——"

The voice from the sofa interrupted the narrator.

"How well I can understand that in him!"

He bent forward slightly.

"Yes. I, too. Everything should be open in love
and war. Open as the day, since both are the call of an
ideal which it is so easy, so terribly easy, to degrade in
the name of Victory."

He paused; then went on:

"I don't know that the commanding officer delved so
deep as that into his feelings. But he did suffer from
them—a sort of disenchanted sadness. It is possible,
even, that he suspected himself of folly. Man is various. But he had no time for much introspection,
because from the southwest a wall of fog had advanced
upon his ship. Great convolutions of vapours flew over,
swirling about masts and funnel, which looked as if they
were beginning to melt. Then they vanished.

"The ship was stopped, all sounds ceased, and the
very fog became motionless, growing denser and as if
solid in its amazing dumb immobility. The men at
their stations lost sight of each other. Footsteps
sounded stealthy; rare voices, impersonal and remote,
died out without resonance. A blind white stillness
took possession of the world.

"It looked, too, as if it would last for days. I don't

mean to say that the fog did not vary a little in its
density.   Now and then it would thin out mysteriously,
revealing to the men a more or less ghostly presentment
of their ship.   Several times the shadow of the coast
itself swam darkly before their eyes through the fluc-
tuating opaque brightness of the great white cloud
clinging to the water.

"Taking advantage of these moments, the ship had
been moved cautiously nearer the shore.   It was useless
to remain out in such thick weather.   Her officers
knew every nook and cranny of the coast along their
beat.   They thought that she would be much better
in a certain cove.   It wasn't a large place, just ample
room for a ship to swing at her anchor.   She would
have an easier time of it till the fog lifted up.

"Slowly, with infinite caution and patience, they
crept closer and closer, seeing no more of the cliffs than
an evanescent dark loom with a narrow border of angry
foam at its foot.   At the moment of anchoring the fog
was so thick that for all they could see they might have
been a thousand miles out in the open sea.   Yet the
shelter of the land could be felt.   There was a peculiar
quality in the stillness of the air.   Very faint, very
elusive, the wash of the ripple against the encircling
land reached their ears, with mysterious sudden pauses.

"The anchor dropped, the leads were laid in.   The
commanding officer went below into his cabin.   But
he had not been there very long when a voice outside
his door requested his presence on deck.   He thought
to himself: 'What is it now?'   He felt some impatience
at being called out again to face the wearisome fog.

"He found that it had thinned again a little and had
taken on a gloomy hue from the dark cliffs which had
no form, no outline, but asserted themselves as a curtain of shadows all round the ship, except in one bright

spot, which was the entrance from the open sea. Several officers were looking that way from the bridge. The second in command met him with the breathlessly whispered information that there was another ship in the cove.

"She had been made out by several pairs of eyes only a couple of minutes before. She was lying at anchor very near the entrance—a mere vague blot on the fog's brightness. And the commanding officer by staring in the direction pointed out to him by eager hands ended by distinguishing it at last himself. Indubitably a vessel of some sort.

"'It's a wonder we didn't run slap into her when coming in,' observed the second in command.

"'Send a boat on board before she vanishes,' said the commanding officer. He surmised that this was a coaster. It could hardly be anything else. But another thought came into his head suddenly. 'It is a wonder,' he said to his second in command, who had rejoined him after sending the boat away.

"By that time both of them had been struck by the fact that the ship so suddenly discovered had not manifested her presence by ringing her bell.

"'We came in very quietly, that's true,' concluded the younger officer. 'But they must have heard our leadsmen at least. We couldn't have passed her more than fifty yards off. The closest shave! They may even have made us out, since they were aware of something coming in. And the strange thing is that we never heard a sound from her. The fellows on board must have been holding their breath.'

"'Aye,' said the commanding officer, thoughtfully.

"In due course the boarding-boat returned, appearing suddenly alongside, as though she had burrowed her way under the fog. The officer in charge came up to make his report, but the commanding officer didn't give him time to begin. He cried from a distance:

"'Coaster, isn't she?'

"'No, sir. A stranger—a neutral,' was the answer.

"'No. Really! Well, tell us all about it. What is she doing here?'

"The young man stated then that he had been told a long and complicated story of engine troubles. But it was plausible enough from a strictly professional point of view and it had the usual features: disablement, dangerous drifting along the shore, weather more or less thick for days, fear of a gale, ultimately a resolve to go in and anchor anywhere on the coast, and so on. Fairly plausible.

"'Engines still disabled?' inquired the commanding officer.

"'No, sir. She has steam on them.'

"The commanding officer took his second aside. 'By Jove!' he said, 'you were right! They were holding their breaths as we passed them. They were.'

"But the second in command had his doubts now.

"'A fog like this does muffle small sounds, sir,' he remarked. 'And what could his object be, after all?'

"'To sneak out unnoticed,' answered the commanding officer.

"'Then why didn't he? He might have done it, you know. Not exactly unnoticed, perhaps. I don't suppose he could have slipped his cable without making some noise. Still, in a minute or so he would have been lost to view—clean gone before we had made him out fairly. Yet he didn't.'

"They looked at each other. The commanding officer shook his head. Such suspicions as the one which had entered his head are not defended easily. He did not even state it openly. The boarding officer finished his report. The cargo of the ship was of a harmless and useful character. She was bound to an English port. Papers and everything in perfect order. Nothing suspicious to be detected anywhere.

"Then passing to the men, he reported the crew on deck as the usual lot. Engineers of the well-known type, and very full of their achievement in repairing the engines. The mate surly. The master rather a fine specimen of a Northman, civil enough, but appeared to have been drinking. Seemed to be recovering from a regular bout of it.

"'I told him I couldn't give him permission to proceed. He said he wouldn't dare to move his ship her own length out in such weather as this, permission or no permission. I left a man on board, though.'

"'Quite right.'

"The commanding officer, after communing with his suspicions for a time, called his second aside.

"'What if she were the very ship which had been feeding some infernal submarine or other?' he said in an undertone.

"The other started. Then, with conviction:

"'She would get off scot-free. You couldn't prove it, sir.'

"'I want to look into it myself.'

"'From the report we've heard I am afraid you couldn't even make a case for reasonable suspicion, sir.'

"'I'll go on board all the same.'

"He had made up his mind. Curiosity is the great motive power of hatred and love. What did he expect to find? He could not have told anybody—not even himself.

"What he really expected to find there was the atmosphere, the atmosphere of gratuitous treachery,

which in his view nothing could excuse; for he thought
that even a passion of unrighteousness for its own sake
could not excuse that. But could he detect it? Sniff
it? Taste it? Receive some mysterious communication which would turn his invincible suspicions into a
certitude strong enough to provoke action with all its
risks?

"The master met him on the after-deck, looming up
in the fog amongst the blurred shapes of the usual ship's
fittings. He was a robust Northman, bearded, and in
the force of his age. A round leather cap fitted his
head closely. His hands were rammed deep into the
pockets of his short leather jacket. He kept them there
while he explained that at sea he lived in the chart-
room, and led the way there, striding carelessly. Just
before reaching the door under the bridge he staggered
a little, recovered himself, flung it open, and stood
aside, leaning his shoulder as if involuntarily against
the side of the house, and staring vaguely into the fog-
filled space. But he followed the commanding officer
at once, flung the door to, snapped on the electric
light, and hastened to thrust his hands back into his
pockets, as though afraid of being seized by them
either in friendship or in hostility.

"The place was stuffy and hot. The usual chart-
rack overhead was full, and the chart on the table
was kept unrolled by an empty cup standing on a saucer
half-full of some spilt dark liquid. A slightly nibbled
biscuit reposed on the chronometer-case. There were
two settees, and one of them had been made up into a
bed with a pillow and some blankets, which were now
very much tumbled. The Northman let himself fall
on it, his hands still in his pockets.

"'Well, here I am,' he said, with a curious air of
being surprised at the sound of his own voice.

"The commanding officer from the other settee observed the handsome, flushed face. Drops of fog hung on the yellow beard and moustaches of the Northman. The much darker eyebrows ran together in a puzzled frown, and suddenly he jumped up.

"'What I mean is that I don't know where I am. I really don't,' he burst out, with extreme earnestness. 'Hang it all! I got turned around somehow. The fog has been after me for a week. More than a week. And then my engines broke down. I will tell you how it was.'

"He burst out into loquacity. It was not hurried, but it was insistent. It was not continuous for all that. It was broken by the most queer, thoughtful pauses. Each of these pauses lasted no more than a couple of seconds, and each had the profoundity of an endless meditation. When he began again nothing betrayed in him the slightest consciousness of these intervals. There was the same fixed glance, the same unchanged earnestness of tone. He didn't know. Indeed, more than one of these pauses occurred in the middle of a sentence.

"The commanding officer listened to the tale. It struck him as more plausible than simple truth is in the habit of being. But that, perhaps, was prejudice. All the time the Northman was speaking the commanding officer had been aware of an inward voice, a grave murmur in the depth of his very own self, telling another tale, as if on purpose to keep alive in him his indignation and his anger with that baseness of greed or of mere outlook which lies often at the root of simple ideas.

"It was the story that had been already told to the boarding officer an hour or so before. The commanding officer nodded slightly at the Northman from time to time. The latter came to an end and turned his eyes away. He added, as an afterthought:

"'Wasn't it enough to drive a man out of his mind with worry? And it's my first voyage to this part, too. And the ship's my own. Your officer has seen the papers. She isn't muck, as you can see for yourself. Just an old cargo-boat. Bare living for my family.'

"He raised a big arm to point at a row of photographs plastering the bulkhead. The movement was ponderous, as if the arm had been made of lead. The commanding officer said, carelessly:

"'You will be making a fortune yet for your family with this old ship.'

"'Yes, if I don't lose her,' said the Northman, gloomily.

"'I mean—out of this war,' added the commanding officer.

"The Northman stared at him in a curiously unseeing and at the same time interested manner, as only eyes of a particular blue shade can stare.

"'And you wouldn't be angry at it,' he said, 'would you? You are too much of a gentleman. We didn't bring this on you. And suppose we sat down and cried. What good would that be? Let those cry who made the trouble,' he concluded, with energy. 'Time's money, you say. Well—*this* time *is* money. Oh! isn't it!'

"The commanding officer tried to keep under the feeling of immense disgust. He said to himself that it was unreasonable. Men were like that—moral cannibals feeding on each other's misfortunes. He said aloud:

"'You have made it perfectly plain how it is that you are here. Your log-book confirms you very minutely. Of course, a log-book may be cooked. Nothing easier.'

"The Northman never moved a muscle. He was gazing at the floor; he seemed not to have heard. He raised his head after a while.

"'But you can't suspect me of anything,' he muttered, negligently.

"The commanding officer thought: 'Why should he say this?'

"Immediately afterwards the man before him added: 'My cargo is for an English port.'

"His voice had turned husky for the moment. The commanding officer reflected: 'That's true. There can be nothing. I can't suspect him. Yet why was he lying with steam up in this fog—and then, hearing us come in, why didn't he give some sign of life? Why? Could it be anything else but a guilty conscience? He could tell by the leadsmen that this was a man-of-war.'

"Yes—why? The commanding officer went on thinking: 'Suppose I ask him and then watch his face. He will betray himself in some way. It's perfectly plain that the fellow *has* been drinking. Yes, he has been drinking; but he will have a lie ready all the same.' The commanding officer was one of those men who are made morally and almost physically uncomfortable by the mere thought of having to beat down a lie. He shrank from the act in scorn and disgust, which were invincible because more temperamental than moral.

"So he went out on deck instead and had the crew mustered formally for his inspection. He found them very much what the report of the boarding officer had led him to expect. And from their answers to his questions he could discover no flaw in the log-book story.

"He dismissed them. His impression of them was—a picked lot; have been promised a fistful of money each if this came off; all slightly anxious, but not frightened. Not a single one of them likely to give the show away. They don't feel in danger of their life. They know England and English ways too well!

"He felt alarmed at catching himself thinking as if his vaguest suspicions were turning into a certitude. For, indeed, there was no shadow of reason for his inferences There was nothing to give away.

"He returned to the chart-room. The Northman had lingered behind there; and something subtly different in his bearing, more bold in his blue, glassy stare, induced the commanding officer to conclude that the fellow had snatched at the opportunity to take another swig at the bottle he must have had concealed somewhere.

"He noticed, too, that the Northman on meeting his eyes put on an elaborately surprised expression. At least, it seemed elaborated. Nothing could be trusted. And the Englishman felt himself with astonishing conviction faced by an enormous lie, solid like a wall, with no way round to get at the truth, whose ugly murderous face he seemed to see peeping over at him with a cynical grin.

"'I dare say,' he began, suddenly, 'you are wondering at my proceedings, though I am not detaining you, am I? You wouldn't dare to move in this fog?'

"'I don't know where I am,' the Northman ejaculated, earnestly. 'I really don't.'

"He looked around as if the very chart-room fittings were strange to him. The commanding officer asked him whether he had not seen any unusual objects floating about while he was at sea.

"'Objects! What objects? We were groping blind in the fog for days.'

"'We had a few clear intervals,' said the commanding officer. 'And I'll tell you what we have seen and the conclusion I've come to about it.'

"He told him in a few words. He heard the sound of a sharp breath indrawn through closed teeth. The Northman with his hand on the table stood absolutely motionless and dumb. He stood as if thunderstruck. Then he produced a fatuous smile.

"Or at least so it appeared to the commanding officer. Was this significant, or of no meaning whatever? He didn't know, he couldn't tell. All the truth had departed out of the world as if drawn in, absorbed in this monstrous villainy this man was—or was not—guilty of.

"'Shooting's too good for people that conceive neutrality in this pretty way,' remarked the commanding officer, after a silence.

"'Yes, yes, yes,' the Northman assented, hurriedly— then added an unexpected and dreamy-voiced 'Perhaps.'

"Was he pretending to be drunk, or only trying to appear sober? His glance was straight, but it was somewhat glazed. His lips outlined themselves firmly under his yellow moustache. But they twitched. Did they twitch? And why was he drooping like this in his attitude?

"'There's no perhaps about it,' pronounced the commanding officer sternly.

"The Northman had straightened himself. And unexpectedly he looked stern, too.

"'No. But what about the tempters? Better kill that lot off. There's about four, five, six million of them,' he said, grimly; but in a moment changed into a whining key. 'But I had better hold my tongue. You have some suspicions.'

"'No, I've no suspicions,' declared the commanding officer.

"He never faltered. At that moment he had the certitude. The air of the chart-room was thick with guilt and falsehood braving the discovery, defying simple right, common decency, all humanity of feeling, every scruple of conduct.

"The Northman drew a long breath. 'Well, we know that you English are gentlemen. But let us speak the truth. Why should we love you so very much? You haven't done anything to be loved. We don't love the other people, of course. They haven't done anything for that either. A fellow comes along with a bag of gold . . . I haven't been in Rotterdam my last voyage for nothing.'

"'You may be able to tell something interesting, then, to our people when you come into port,' interjected the officer.

"I might. But you keep some people in your pay at Rotterdam. Let them report. I am a neutral—am I not? . . . Have you ever seen a poor man on one side and a bag of gold on the other? Of course, I couldn't be tempted. I haven't the nerve for it. Really I haven't. It's nothing to me. I am just talking openly for once.'

"'Yes. And I am listening to you,' said the commanding officer, quietly.

"The Northman leaned forward over the table. 'Now that I know you have no suspicions, I talk. You don't know what a poor man is. I do. I am poor myself. This old ship, she isn't much, and she is mortgaged, too. Bare living, no more. Of course, I wouldn't have the nerve. But a man who has nerve! See. The stuff he takes aboard looks like any other cargo—packages, barrels, tins, copper tubes—what not. He doesn't see it work. It isn't real to him. But he sees the gold. That's real. Of course, nothing could induce me. I suffer from an internal disease. I would either go crazy from anxiety—or—or—take to drink or something. The risk is too great. Why—ruin!'

"'It should be death.' The commanding officer got up, after this curt declaration, which the other received with a hard stare oddly combined with an uncertain smile. The officer's gorge rose at the atmosphere of murderous complicity which surrounded him, denser, more impenetrable, more acrid than the fog outside.

"'It's nothing to me,' murmured the Northman, swaying visibly.

"'Of course not,' assented the commanding officer, with a great effort to keep his voice calm and low. The certitude was strong within him. 'But I am going to clear all you fellows off this coast at once. And I will begin with you. You must leave in half an hour.'

"By that time the officer was walking along the deck with the Northman at his elbow.

"'What! In this fog?' the latter cried out, huskily.

"'Yes, you will have to go in this fog.'

"'But I don't know where I am. I really don't.'

"The commanding officer turned round. A sort of fury possessed him. The eyes of the two men met. Those of the Northman expressed a profound amazement.

"'Oh, you don't know how to get out.' The commanding officer spoke with composure, but his heart was beating with anger and dread. 'I will give you your course. Steer south-by-east-half-east for about four miles and then you will be clear to haul to the eastward for your port. The weather will clear up before very long.'

"'Must I? What could induce me? I haven't the nerve.'

"'And yet you must go. Unless you want to——'

"'I don't want to,' panted the Northman. 'I've enough of it.'

"The commanding officer got over the side. The Northman remained still as if rooted to the deck. Before his boat reached his ship the commanding officer heard the steamer beginning to pick up her anchor. Then, shadowy in the fog, she steamed out on the given course.

"'Yes,' he said to his officers, 'I let him go.'"

The narrator bent forward towards the couch, where no movement betrayed the presence of a living person.

"Listen," he said, forcibly. "That course would lead the Northman straight on a deadly ledge of rock. And the commanding officer gave it to him. He steamed out—ran on it—and went down. So he had spoken the truth. He did not know where he was. But it proves nothing. Nothing either way. It may have been the only truth in all his story. And yet . . . He seems to have been driven out by a menacing stare—nothing more."

He abandoned all pretence.

"Yes, I gave that course to him. It seemed to me a supreme test. I believe—no, I don't believe. I don't know. At the time I was certain. They all went down; and I don't know whether I have done stern retribution—or murder; whether I have added to the corpses that litter the bed of the unreadable sea the bodies of men completely innocent or basely guilty. I don't know. I shall never know."

He rose. The woman on the couch got up and threw her arms round his neck. Her eyes put two gleams in the deep shadow of the room. She knew his passion for truth, his horror of deceit, his humanity.

"Oh, my poor, poor——"

"I shall never know," he repeated, sternly, disengaged himself, pressed her hands to his lips, and went out.

THE BLACK MATE

THE BLACK MATE

A GOOD many years ago there were several ships loading at the Jetty, London Dock. I am speaking here of the 'eighties of the last century, of the time when London had plenty of fine ships in the docks, though not so many fine buildings in its streets.

The ships at the Jetty were fine enough; they lay one behind the other; and the *Sapphire*, third from the end, was as good as the rest of them, and nothing more. Each ship at the Jetty had, of course, her chief officer on board. So had every other ship in dock.

The policeman at the gates knew them all by sight, without being able to say at once, without thinking, to what ship any particular man belonged. As a matter of fact, the mates of the ships then lying in the London Dock were like the majority of officers in the Merchant Service—a steady, hard-working, staunch, unromantic-looking set of men, belonging to various classes of society, but with the professional stamp obliterating the personal characteristics, which were not very marked anyhow.

This last was true of them all, with the exception of the mate of the *Sapphire*. Of him the policemen could not be in doubt. This one had a presence.

He was noticeable to them in the street from a great distance; and when in the morning he strode down the Jetty to his ship, the lumpers and the dock labourers rolling the bales and trundling the cases of cargo on their hand-trucks would remark to each other:

"Here's the black mate coming along."

That was the name they gave him, being a gross lot, who could have no appreciation of the man's dignified bearing. And to call him black was the superficial impressionism of the ignorant.

Of course, Mr. Bunter, the mate of the *Sapphire*, was not black. He was no more black than you or I, and certainly as white as any chief mate of a ship in the whole of the Port of London. His complexion was of the sort that did not take the tan easily; and I happen to know that the poor fellow had had a month's illness just before he joined the *Sapphire*.

From this you will perceive that I knew Bunter. Of course I knew him. And, what's more, I knew his secret at the time, this secret which—never mind just now. Returning to Bunter's personal appearance, it was nothing but ignorant prejudice on the part of the foreman stevedore to say, as he did in my hearing: "I bet he's a furriner of some sort." A man may have black hair without being set down for a Dago. I have known a West-country sailor, boatswain of a fine ship, who looked more Spanish than any Spaniard afloat I've ever met. He looked like a Spaniard in a picture.

Competent authorities tell us that this earth is to be finally the inheritance of men with dark hair and brown eyes. It seems that already the great majority of mankind is dark-haired in various shades. But it is only when you meet one that you notice how men with really black hair, black as ebony, are rare. Bunter's hair was absolutely black, black as a raven's wing. He wore, too, all his beard (clipped, but a good length all the same), and his eyebrows were thick and bushy. Add to this steely blue eyes, which in a fair-haired man would have been nothing so extraordinary, but in that sombre framing made a startling contrast, and you will easily understand that Bunter was noticeable enough

If it had not been for the quietness of his movements, for the general soberness of his demeanour, one would have given him credit for a fiercely passionate nature.

Of course, he was not in his first youth; but if the expression "in the force of his age" has any meaning, he realized it completely. He was a tall man, too, though rather spare. Seeing him from his poop indefatigably busy with his duties, Captain Ashton, of the clipper ship *Elsinore*, lying just ahead of the *Sapphire*, remarked once to a friend that "Johns has got somebody there to hustle his ship along for him."

Captain Johns, master of the *Sapphire*, having commanded ships for many years, was well known without being much respected or liked. In the company of his fellows he was either neglected or chaffed. The chaffing was generally undertaken by Captain Ashton, a cynical and teasing sort of man. It was Captain Ashton who permitted himself the unpleasant joke of proclaiming once in company that "Johns is of the opinion that every sailor above forty years of age ought to be poisoned—shipmasters in actual command excepted."

It was in a City restaurant, where several well-known shipmasters were having lunch together. There was Captain Ashton, florid and jovial, in a large white waistcoat and with a yellow rose in his buttonhole; Captain Sellers in a sack-coat, thin and pale-faced, with his iron-gray hair tucked behind his ears, and, but for the absence of spectacles, looking like an ascetical mild man of books; Captain Hell, a bluff sea-dog with hairy fingers, in blue serge and a black felt hat pushed far back off his crimson forehead. There was also a very young shipmaster, with a little fair moustache and serious eyes, who said nothing, and only smiled faintly from time to time.

Captain Johns, very much startled, raised his perplexed and credulous glance, which, together with a low and horizontally wrinkled brow, did not make a very intellectual *ensemble*. This impression was by no means mended by the slightly pointed form of his bald head.

Everybody laughed outright, and, thus guided, Captain Johns ended by smiling rather sourly, and attempted to defend himself. It was all very well to joke, but nowadays, when ships, to pay anything at all, had to be driven hard on the passage and in harbour, the sea was no place for elderly men. Only young men and men in their prime were equal to modern conditions of push and hurry. Look at the great firms: almost every single one of them was getting rid of men showing any signs of age. He, for one, didn't want any oldsters on board his ship.

And, indeed, in this opinion Captain Johns was not singular. There was at that time a lot of seamen, with nothing against them but that they were grizzled, wearing out the soles of their last pair of boots on the pavements of the City in the heart-breaking search for a berth.

Captain Johns added with a sort of ill-humoured innocence that from holding that opinion to thinking of poisoning people was a very long step.

This seemed final but Captain Ashton would not let go his joke.

"Oh, yes. I am sure you would. You said distinctly 'of no use.' What's to be done with men who are 'of no use?' You are a kind-hearted fellow, Johns. I am sure that if only you thought it over carefully you would consent to have them poisoned in some painless manner."

Captain Sellers twitched his thin, sinuous lips.

"Make ghosts of them," he suggested, pointedly.

At the mention of ghosts Captain Johns became shy, in his perplexed, sly, and unlovely manner.

Captain Ashton winked.

"Yes. And then perhaps you would get a chance to have a communication with the world of spirits. Surely the ghosts of seamen should haunt ships. Some of them would be sure to call on an old shipmate."

Captain Sellers remarked drily:

"Don't raise his hopes like this. It's cruel. He won't see anything. You know, Johns, that nobody has ever seen a ghost."

At this intolerable provocation Captain Johns came out of his reserve. With no perplexity whatever, but with a positive passion of credulity giving momentary lustre to his dull little eyes, he brought up a lot of authenticated instances. There were books and books full of instances. It was merest ignorance to deny supernatural apparitions. Cases were published every month in a special newspaper. Professor Cranks saw ghosts daily. And Professor Cranks was no small potatoes either. One of the biggest scientific men living. And there was that newspaper fellow—what's his name?—who had a girl-ghost visitor. He printed in his paper things she said to him. And to say there were no ghosts after that!

"Why, they have been photographed! What more proof do you want?"

Captain Johns was indignant. Captain Bell's lips twitched, but Captain Ashton protested now.

"For goodness' sake don't keep him going with that. And by the by, Johns, who's that hairy pirate you've got for your new mate? Nobody in the Dock seems to have seen him before."

Captain Johns, pacified by the change of subjects,

*D

answered simply that Willy, the tobacconist at the corner of Fenchurch Street, had sent him along.

Willy, his shop, and the very house in Fenchurch Street, I believe, are gone now. In his time, wearing a careworn, absent-minded look on his pasty face, Willy served with tobacco many southern-going ships out of the Port of London. At certain times of the day the shop would be full of shipmasters. They sat on casks, they lounged against the counter.

Many a youngster found his first lift in life there; many a man got a sorely needed berth by simply dropping in for four pennyworth of birds'-eye at an auspicious moment. Even Willy's assistant, a redheaded, uninterested, delicate-looking young fellow, would hand you across the counter sometimes a bit of valuable intelligence with your box of cigarettes, in a whisper, lips hardly moving, thus: "The *Bellona*, South Dock. Second officer wanted. You may be in time for it if you hurry up."

And didn't one just fly!

"Oh, Willy sent him," said Captain Ashton. "He's a very striking man. If you were to put a red sash round his waist and a red handkerchief round his head he would look exactly like one of them buccaneering chaps that made men walk the plank and carried women off into captivity. Look out, Johns, he don't cut your throat for you and run off with the *Sapphire*. What ship has he come out of last?"

Captain Johns, after looking up credulously as usual, wrinkled his brow, and said placidly that the man had seen better days. His name was Bunter.

"He's had command of a Liverpool ship, the *Samaria*, some years ago. He lost her in the Indian Ocean, and had his certificate suspended for a year. Ever since then he has not been able to get another command.

He's been knocking about in the Western Ocean trade lately."

"That accounts for him being a stranger to everybody about the Docks," Captain Ashton concluded as they rose from table.

Captain Johns walked down to the Dock after lunch. He was short of stature and slightly bandy. His appearance did not inspire the generality of mankind with esteem; but it must have been otherwise with his employers. He had the reputation of being an uncomfortable commander, meticulous in trifles, always nursing a grievance of some sort and incessantly nagging. He was not a man to kick up a row with you and be done with it, but to say nasty things in a whining voice; a man capable of making one's life a perfect misery if he took a dislike to an officer.

That very evening I went to see Bunter on board, and sympathized with him on his prospects for the voyage. He was subdued. I suppose a man with a secret locked up in his breast loses his buoyancy. And there was another reason why I could not expect Bunter to show a great elasticity of spirits. For one thing he had been very seedy lately, and besides—but of that later.

Captain Johns had been on board that afternoon and had loitered and dodged about his chief mate in a manner which had annoyed Bunter exceedingly.

"What could he mean?" he asked with calm exasperation. "One would think he suspected I had stolen something and tried to see in what pocket I had stowed it away; or that somebody told him I had a tail and he wanted to find out how I managed to conceal it. I don't like to be approached from behind several times in one afternoon in that creepy way and then to be looked up at suddenly in front from under my elbow.

Is it a new sort of peep-bo game? It doesn't amuse me. I am no longer a baby."

I assured him that if anyone were to tell Captain Johns that he—Bunter—had a tail, Johns would manage to get himself to believe the story in some mysterious manner. He would. He was suspicious and credulous to an inconceivable degree. He would believe any silly tale, suspect any man of anything, and crawl about with it and ruminate the stuff, and turn it over and over in his mind in the most miserable, inwardly whining perplexity. He would take the meanest possible view in the end, and discover the meanest possible course of action by a sort of natural genius for that sort of thing.

Bunter also told me that the mean creature had crept all over the ship on his little, bandy legs, taking him along to grumble and whine to about a lot of trifles. Crept about the decks like a wretched insect—like a cockroach, only not so lively.

Thus did the self-possessed Bunter express himself with great disgust. Then, going on with his usual stately deliberation, made sinister by the frown of his jet-black eyebrows:

"And the fellow is mad, too. He tried to be sociable for a bit, and could find nothing else but to make big eyes at me, and ask me if I believed 'in communication beyond the grave.' Communication beyond—I didn't know what he meant at first. I didn't know what to say. 'A very solemn subject, Mr. Bunter,' says he. 'I've given a great deal of study to it.'"

Had Johns lived on shore he would have been the predestined prey of fraudulent mediums; or even if he had had any decent opportunities between the voyages. Luckily for him, when in England, he lived somewhere far away in Leytonstone, with a maiden sister ten years older than himself, a fearsome virago twice his size, before whom he trembled. It was said she bullied him terribly in general; and in the particular instance of his spiritualistic leanings she had her own views.

These leanings were to her simply satanic. She was reported as having declared that, "With God's help, she would prevent that fool from giving himself up to the Devils." It was beyond doubt that Johns' secret ambition was to get into personal communication with the spirits of the dead—if only his sister would let him. But she was adamant. I was told that while in London he had to account to her for every penny of the money he took with him in the morning, and for every hour of his time. And she kept the bankbook, too.

Bunter (he had been a wild youngster, but he was well connected; had ancestors; there was a family tomb somewhere in the home counties)—Bunter was indignant, perhaps on account of his own dead. Those steely-blue eyes of his flashed with positive ferocity out of that black-bearded face. He impressed me— there was so much dark passion in his leisurely contempt.

"The cheek of the fellow! Enter into relations with . . . A mean little cad like this! It would be an impudent intrusion. He wants to enter! . . . What is it? A new sort of snobbishness or what?"

I laughed outright at this original view of spiritism— or whatever the ghost craze is called. Even Bunter himself condescended to smile. But it was an austere, quickly vanished smile. A man in his almost, I may say, tragic position couldn't be expected—you understand. He was really worried. He was ready eventually to put up with any dirty trick in the course of the voyage. A man could not expect much consideration should he find himself at the mercy of a fellow like Johns. A misfortune is a misfortune, and there's an end of it. But to be bored by mean, low-spirited, inane ghost stories in the Johns style, all the way out to Calcutta and back again, was an intolerable apprehension to be under. Spiritism was indeed a solemn subject to think about in that light. Dreadful, even!

Poor fellow! Little we both thought that before very long he himself . . . However, I could give him no comfort. I was rather appalled myself.

Bunter had also another annoyance that day. A confounded berthing master came on board on some pretence or other, but in reality, Bunter thought, simply impelled by an inconvenient curiosity—inconvenient to Bunter, that is. After some beating about the bush, that man suddenly said:

"I can't help thinking. I've seen you before somewhere, Mr. Mate. If I heard your name, perhaps ——"

Bunter—that's the worst of a life with a mystery in it—was much alarmed. It was very likely that the man had seen him before—worse luck to his excellent memory. Bunter himself could not be expected to remember every casual dock walloper he might have had to do with. Bunter brazened it out by turning upon the man, making use of that impressive, black-as-night sternness of expression his unusual hair furnished him with:

"My name's Bunter, sir. Does that enlighten your inquisitive intellect? And I don't ask what your name may be. I don't want to know. I've no use for it, sir. An individual who calmly tells me to my face that he is *not sure* if he has seen me before, either means to be impudent or is no better than a worm, sir. Yes, I said a worm—a blind worm!"

Brave Bunter. That was the line to take. He fairly drove the beggar out of the ship, as if every word had been a blow. But the pertinacity of that brass-bound Paul Pry was astonishing. He cleared out of the ship, of course, before Bunter's ire, not saying anything, and only trying to cover up his retreat by a sickly smile. But once on the Jetty he turned deliberately round, and set himself to stare in dead earnest at the ship. He remained planted there like a mooring-post, absolutely motionless, and with his stupid eyes winking no more than a pair of cabin portholes.

What could Bunter do? It was awkward for him, you know. He could not go and put his head into the bread-locker. What he did was to take up a position abaft the mizzen-rigging, and stare back as unwinking as the other. So they remained, and I don't know which of them grew giddy first; but the man on the Jetty, not having the advantage of something to hold on to, got tired the soonest, flung his arm, giving the contest up, as it were, and went away at last

Bunter told me he was glad the *Sapphire*, "that gem amongst ships" as he alluded to her sarcastically, was going to sea next day. He had had enough of the Dock. I understood his impatience. He had steeled himself against any possible worry the voyage might bring, though it is clear enough now that he was not prepared for the extraordinary experience that was awaiting him already, and in no other part of the world than the Indian Ocean itself; the very part of the world where the poor fellow had lost his ship and had broken his luck, as it seemed for good and all, at the same time.

As to his remorse in regard to a certain secret action of his life, well, I understand that a man of Bunter's fine character would suffer not a little. Still, between ourselves, and without the slightest wish to be cynical, it cannot be denied that with the noblest of us the fear of being found out enters for some considerable part into the composition of remorse. I didn't say this in so many words to Bunter, but, as the poor fellow harped a bit on it, I told him that there were skeletons in a good many honest cupboards, and that, as to his own particular guilt, it wasn't writ large on his face for everybody to see—so he needn't worry as to that. And besides, he would be gone to sea in about twelve hours from now.

He said there was some comfort in that thought, and went off then to spend his last evening for many months with his wife. For all his wildness, Bunter had made no mistake in his marrying. He had married a lady. A perfect lady. She was a dear little woman, too. As to her pluck, I, who know what times they had to go through, I cannot admire her enough for it. Real, hard-wearing every day and day after day pluck that only a woman is capable of when she is of the right sort—the undismayed sort I would call it.

The black mate felt this parting with his wife more than any of the previous ones in all the years of bad luck. But she was of the undismayed kind, and showed less trouble in her gentle face than the black-haired, buccaneer-like, but dignified mate of the *Sapphire*. It may be that her conscience was less disturbed than her husband's. Of course, his life had no secret places for her; but a woman's conscience is somewhat more resourceful in finding good and valid excuses. It depends greatly on the person that needs them, too.

They had agreed that she should not come down to the Dock to see him off. "I wonder you care to look at me at all," said the sensitive man. And she did not laugh.

Bunter was very sensitive; he left her rather brusquely at the last. He got on board in good time, and produced the usual impression on the mud-pilot in the broken-down straw hat who took the *Sapphire* out of dock. The river-man was very polite to the dignified, striking-looking chief mate. "The five-inch manilla for the check-rope, Mr.— Bunter, thank you—Mr. Bunter, please." The sea-pilot who left the "gem of ships" heading comfortably down Channel off Dover told some of his friends that, this voyage, the *Sapphire* had for chief mate a man who seemed a jolly sight too good for old Johns. "Bunter's his name. I wonder where he's sprung from? Never seen him before in any ship I piloted in or out all these years. He's the sort of man you don't forget. You couldn't. A thorough good sailor, too. And won't old Johns just worry his head off! Unless the old fool should take fright at him—for he does not seem the sort of man that would let himself be put upon without letting you know what he thinks of you. And that's exactly what old Johns would be more afraid of than of anything else."

As this is really meant to be the record of a spiritualistic experience which came, if not precisely to Captain Johns himself, at any rate to his ship, there is no use in recording the other events of the passage out. It was an ordinary passage, the crew was an ordinary crew, the weather was of the usual kind. The black mate's quiet, sedate method of going to work had given a sober tone to the life of the ship. Even in gales of wind everything went on quietly somehow.

There was only one severe blow which made things fairly lively for all hands for full four-and-twenty hours. That was off the coast of Africa, after passing the Cape of Good Hope. At the very height of it several heavy seas were shipped with no serious results, but there was a considerable smashing of breakable objects in the pantry and in the staterooms. Mr. Bunter, who was so greatly respected on board, found himself treated scurvily by the Southern Ocean, which, bursting open the door of his room like a ruffianly burglar, carried off several useful things, and made all the others extremely wet.

Later, on the same day, the Southern Ocean caused the *Sapphire* to lurch over in such an unrestrained fashion that the two drawers fitted under Mr. Bunter's sleeping-berth flew out altogether, spilling all their contents. They ought, of course, to have been locked, and Mr. Bunter had only to thank himself for what had happened. He ought to have turned the key on each before going out on deck.

His consternation was very great. The steward, who was paddling about all the time with swabs, trying to dry out the flooded cuddy, heard him exclaim "Hallo!" in a startled and dismayed tone. In the midst of his work the steward felt a sympathetic concern for the mate's distress.

Captain Johns was secretly glad when he heard of the damage. He was indeed afraid of his chief mate, as the sea-pilot had ventured to foretell, and afraid of him for the very reason the sea-pilot had put forward as likely.

Captain Johns, therefore, would have liked very much to hold that black mate of his at his mercy in some way or other. But the man was irreproachable, as near absolute perfection as could be. And Captain Johns was much annoyed, and at the same time congratulated himself on his chief officer's efficiency.

He made a great show of living sociably with him, on the principle that the more friendly you are with a man the more easily you may catch him tripping; and also for the reason that he wanted to have somebody who would listen to his stories of manifestations, apparitions, ghosts, and all the rest of the imbecile spook-lore. He had it all at his fingers' ends; and he spun those ghostly yarns in a persistent, colourless voice, giving them a futile turn peculiarly his own.

"I like to converse with my officers," he used to say. "There are masters that hardly ever open their mouths from beginning to end of a passage for fear of losing their dignity. What's that, after all—this bit of position a man holds!"

His sociability was most to be dreaded in the second dog-watch, because he was one of those men who grow lively towards the evening, and the officer on duty was unable then to find excuses for leaving the poop. Captain Johns would pop up the companion suddenly, and, sidling up in his creeping way to poor Bunter, as he walked up and down, would fire into him some spiritualistic proposition, such as:

"Spirits, male and female, show a good deal of refinement in a general way, don't they?"

To which Bunter, holding his black-whiskered head high, would mutter:

"I don't know."

"Ah! that's because you don't want to. You are the most obstinate, prejudiced man I've ever met, Mr. Bunter. I told you you may have any book out of my bookcase. You may just go into my stateroom and help yourself to any volume."

And if Bunter protested that he was too tired in his watches below to spare any time for reading, Captain Johns would smile nastily behind his back, and remark that of course some people needed more sleep than others to keep themselves fit for their work. If Mr. Bunter was afraid of not keeping properly awake when on duty at night, that was another matter.

"But I think you borrowed a novel to read from the second mate the other day—a trashy pack of lies," Captain Johns sighed. "I am afraid you are not a spiritually minded man, Mr. Bunter. That's what's the matter."

Sometimes he would appear on deck in the middle of the night, looking very grotesque and bandy-legged in his sleeping suit. At that sight the persecuted Bunter would wring his hands stealthily, and break out into moisture all over his forehead. After standing sleepily by the binnacle, scratching himself in an unpleasant manner, Captain Johns was sure to start on some aspect or other of his only topic.

He would, for instance, discourse on the improvement of morality to be expected from the establishment of general and close intercourse with the spirits of the departed. The spirits, Captain Johns thought, would consent to associate familiarly with the living if it were not for the unbelief of the great mass of mankind. He himself would not care to have anything to do with a crowd that would not believe in his—Captain Johns'— existence. Then why should a spirit? This was asking too much.

He went on breathing hard by the binnacle and trying to reach round his shoulder-blades; then, with a thick, drowsy severity, declared:

"Incredulity, sir, is the evil of the age!"

It rejected the evidence of Professor Cranks and of the journalist chap. It resisted the production of photographs.

For Captain Johns believed firmly that certain spirits had been photographed. He had read something of it in the papers. And the idea of it having been done had got a tremendous hold on him, because his mind was not critical. Bunter said afterwards that nothing could be more weird than this little man, swathed in a sleeping suit three sizes too large for him, shuffling with excitement in the moonlight near the wheel, and shaking his fist at the serene sea.

"Photographs! photographs!" he would repeat, in a voice as creaky as a rusty hinge.

The very helmsman just behind him got uneasy at that performance, not being capable of understanding exactly what the "old man was kicking up a row with the mate about."

Then Johns, after calming down a bit, would begin again.

"The sensitised plate can't lie. No, sir."

Nothing could be more funny than this ridiculous little man's conviction—his dogmatic tone. Bunter would go on swinging up and down the poop like a deliberate, dignified pendulum. He said not a word. But the poor fellow had not a trifle on his conscience, as you know; and to have imbecile ghosts rammed down his throat like this on top of his own worry nearly drove him crazy. He knew that on many occasions he was on the verge of lunacy, because he could not help indulging in half-delirious visions of Captain Johns being picked up by the scruff of the neck and dropped over the taffrail into the ship's wake—the sort of thing no sane sailorman would think of doing to a cat or any other animal, anyhow. He imagined him bobbing up—a tiny black speck left far astern on the moonlit ocean.

I don't think that even at the worst moments Bunter really desired to drown Captain Johns. I fancy that all his disordered imagination longed for was merely to stop the ghostly inanity of the skipper's talk.

But, all the same, it was a dangerous form of self-indulgence. Just picture to yourself that ship in the

Indian Ocean, on a clear, tropical night, with her sails full and still, the watch on deck stowed away out of sight; and on her poop, flooded with moonlight, the stately black mate walking up and down with measured, dignified steps, preserving an awful silence, and that grotesquely mean little figure in striped flannelette alternately creaking and droning of "personal intercourse beyond the grave."

It makes me creepy all over to think of. And sometimes the folly of Captain Johns would appear clothed in a sort of weird utilitarianism. How useful it would be if the spirits of the departed could be induced to take a practical interest in the affairs of the living! What a help, say, to the police, for instance, in the detection of crime! The number of murders, at any rate, would be considerably reduced, he guessed with an air of great sagacity. Then he would give way to grotesque discouragement.

Where was the use of trying to communicate with people that had no faith, and more likely than not would scorn the offered information? Spirits had their feelings. They were *all* feelings in a way. But he was surprised at the forbearance shown towards murderers by their victims. That was the sort of apparition that no guilty man would dare to pooh-pooh. And perhaps the undiscovered murderers—whether believing or not—were haunted. They wouldn't be likely to boast about it, would they?

"For myself," he pursued, in a sort of vindictive, malevolent whine, "if anybody murdered me I would not let him forget it. I would wither him up—I would terrify him to death."

The idea of his skipper's ghost terrifying anyone was so ludicrous that the black mate, little disposed to mirth as he was, could not help giving vent to a weary laugh

And this laugh, the only acknowledgment of a long and earnest discourse, offended Captain Johns.

"What's there to laugh at in this conceited manner, Mr. Bunter?" he snarled. "Supernatural visitations have terrified better men than you. Don't you allow me enough soul to make a ghost of?"

I think it was the nasty tone that caused Bunter to stop short and turn about.

"I shouldn't wonder," went on the angry fanatic of spiritism, "if you weren't one of them people that take no more account of a man than if he were a beast. You would be capable, I don't doubt, to deny the possession of an immortal soul to your own father."

And then Bunter, being bored beyond endurance, and also exasperated by the private worry, lost his self-possession.

He walked up suddenly to Captain Johns, and, stooping a little to look close into his face, said, in a low, even tone:

"You don't know what a man like me is capable of."

Captain Johns threw his head back, but was too astonished to budge. Bunter resumed his walk; and for a long time his measured footsteps and the low wash of the water alongside were the only sounds which troubled the silence brooding over the great waters. Then Captain Johns cleared his throat uneasily, and, after sidling away towards the companion for greater safety, plucked up enough courage to retreat under an act of authority:

"Raise the starboard clew of the mainsail, and lay the yards dead square, Mr. Bunter. Don't you see the wind is nearly right aft?"

Bunter at once answered "Ay, ay, sir," though there was not the slightest necessity to touch the yards, and the wind was well out on the quarter. While he was executing the order Captain Johns hung on the companion-steps, growling to himself: "Walk this poop like an admiral and don't even notice when the yards want trimming!"—loud enough for the helmsman to overhear. Then he sank slowly backwards out of the man's sight; and when he reached the bottom of the stairs he stood still and thought.

"He's an awful ruffian, with all his gentlemanly airs. No more gentleman mates for me."

Two nights afterwards he was slumbering peacefully in his berth, when a heavy thumping just above his head (a well-understood signal that he was wanted on deck) made him leap out of bed, broad awake in a moment.

"What's up?" he muttered, running out barefooted. On passing through the cabin he glanced at the clock. It was the middle watch. "What on earth can the mate want me for?" he thought.

Bolting out of the companion, he found a clear, dewy moonlit night and a strong, steady breeze. He looked around wildly. There was no one on the poop except the helmsman, who addressed him at once.

"It was me, sir. I let go the wheel for a second to stamp over your head. I am afraid there's something wrong with the mate."

"Where's he got to?" asked the captain sharply.

The man, who was obviously nervous, said:

"The last I saw of him was as he fell down the port poop-ladder."

"Fell down the poop-ladder! What did he do that for? What made him?"

"I don't know, sir. He was walking the port side. Then just as he turned towards me to come aft . . ."

"You saw him?" interrupted the captain.

"I did. I was looking at him. And I heard the crash, too—something awful. Like the mainmast going overboard. It was as if something had struck him."

Captain Johns became very uneasy and alarmed.

"Come," he said sharply. "Did anybody strike him? What did you see?"

"Nothing, sir, so help me! There was nothing to see. He just gave a little sort of hallo! threw his hands before him, and over he went—crash. I couldn't hear anything more, so I just let go the wheel for a second to call you up."

"You're scared!" said Captain Johns.

"I am, sir, straight!"

Captain Johns stared at him. The silence of his ship driving on her way seemed to contain a danger—a mystery. He was reluctant to go and look for his mate himself, in the shadows of the main-deck, so quiet, so still.

All he did was to advance to the break of the poop, and call for the watch. As the sleepy men came trooping aft, he shouted to them fiercely:

"Look at the foot of the port poop-ladder, some of you! See the mate lying there?"

Their startled exclamations told him immediately that they did see him. Somebody even screeched out emotionally:

"He's dead!"

Mr. Bunter was laid in his bunk and when the lamp in his room was lit he looked indeed as if he were dead, but it was obvious also that he was breathing yet. The steward had been roused out, the second mate called and sent on deck to look after the ship, and for an hour or so Captain Johns devoted himself silently to the restoring of consciousness. Mr. Bunter at last opened his eyes, but he could not speak. He was dazed and inert. The steward bandaged a nasty scalp-wound while Captain Johns held an additional light. They had to cut away a lot of Mr. Bunter's jet-black hair to make a good dressing. This done, and after gazing for a while at their patient, the two left the cabin.

"A rum go, this, steward," said Captain Johns in the passage.

"Yessir."

"A sober man that's right in his head does not fall down a poop-ladder like a sack of potatoes. The ship's as steady as a church."

"Yessir. Fit of some kind, I shouldn't wonder."

"Well, I should. He doesn't look as if he were subject to fits and giddiness. Why, the man's in the prime of life. I wouldn't have another kind of mate—not if I knew it. You don't think he has a private store of liquor, do you, eh? He seemed to me a bit strange in his manner several times lately. Off his feed, too, a bit, I noticed."

"Well, sir, if he ever had a bottle or two of grog in his cabin, that must have gone a long time ago. I saw him throw some broken glass overboard after the last gale we had; but that didn't amount to anything. Anyway, sir, you couldn't call Mr. Bunter a drinking man."

"No," conceded the captain, reflectively. And the steward, locking the pantry door, tried to escape out of the passage, thinking he could manage to snatch another hour of sleep before it was time for him to turn out for the day.

Captain Johns shook his head.

"There's some mystery there."

"There's special Providence that he didn't crack his head like an eggshell on the quarter-deck mooring-bits, sir. The men tell me he couldn't have missed them by more than an inch."

And the steward vanished skilfully.

Captain Johns spent the rest of the night and the whole of the ensuing day between his own room and that of the mate.

In his own room he sat with his open hands reposing on his knees, his lips pursed up, and the horizontal furrows on his forehead marked very heavily. Now and then raising his arm by a slow, as if cautious movement, he scratched lightly the top of his bald head. In the mate's room he stood for long periods of time with his hand to his lips, gazing at the half-conscious man.

For three days Mr. Bunter did not say a single word. He looked at people sensibly enough but did not seem to be able to hear any questions put to him. They cut off some more of his hair and swathed his head in wet cloths. He took some nourishment, and was made as comfortable as possible. At dinner on the third day the second mate remarked to the captain, in connection with the affair:

"These half-round brass plates on the steps of the poop-ladders are beastly dangerous things!"

"Are they?" retorted Captain Johns, sourly. "It takes more than a brass plate to account for an able-bodied man crashing down in this fashion like a felled ox."

The second mate was impressed by that view. There was something in that, he thought.

"And the weather fine, everything dry, and the ship going along as steady as a church!" pursued Captain Johns, gruffly.

As Captain Johns continued to look extremely sour, the second mate did not open his lips any more during the dinner. Captain Johns was annoyed and hurt by an innocent remark, because the fitting of the aforesaid brass plates had been done at his suggestion only the voyage before, in order to smarten up the appearance of the poop-ladders.

On the fourth day Mr. Bunter looked decidedly better; very languid yet, of course, but he heard and understood what was said to him, and even could say a few words in a feeble voice.

Captain Johns, coming in, contemplated him attentively, without much visible sympathy.

"Well, can you give us your account of this accident, Mr. Bunter?"

Bunter moved slightly his bandaged head, and fixed his cold blue stare on Captain Johns' face, as if taking stock and appraising the value of every feature; the perplexed forehead, the credulous eyes, the inane droop of the mouth. And he gazed so long that Captain Johns grew restive, and looked over his shoulder at the door.

"No accident," breathed out Bunter, in a peculiar tone.

"You don't mean to say you've got the falling sickness," said Captain Johns. "How would you call it signing as chief mate of a clipper ship with a thing like that on you?"

Bunter answered him only by a sinister look. The skipper shuffled his feet a little.

"Well, what made you have that tumble, then?"

Bunter raised himself a little, and, looking straight into Captain Johns' eyes said, in a very distinct whisper:

"You—were—right!"

He fell back and closed his eyes. Not a word more could Captain Johns get out of him; and, the steward coming into the cabin, the skipper withdrew.

But that very night, unobserved, Captain Johns,

opening the door cautiously, entered again the mate's cabin. He could wait no longer. The suppressed eagerness, the excitement expressed in all his mean, creeping little person, did not escape the chief mate, who was lying awake, looking frightfully pulled down and perfectly impassive.

"You are coming to gloat over me, I suppose," said Bunter without moving, and yet making a palpable hit.

"Bless my soul!" exclaimed Captain Johns with a start, and assuming a sobered demeanour. "There's a thing to say!"

"Well, gloat, then! You and your ghosts, you've managed to get over a live man."

This was said by Bunter without stirring, in a low voice, and with not much expression.

"Do you mean to say," inquired Captain Johns, in awe-struck whisper, "that you had a supernatural experience that night? You saw an apparition, then, on board my ship?"

Reluctance, shame, disgust, would have been visible on poor Bunter's countenance if the great part of it had not been swathed up in cotton-wool and bandages. His ebony eyebrows, more sinister than ever amongst all that lot of white linen, came together in a frown as he made a mighty effort to say:

"Yes, I have seen."

The wretchedness in his eyes would have awakened the compassion of any other man than Captain Johns. But Captain Johns was all agog with triumphant excitement. He was just a little bit frightened, too. He looked at that unbelieving scoffer laid low, and did not even dimly guess at his profound, humiliating distress. He was not generally capable of taking much part in the anguish of his fellow-creatures. This time, moreover, he was excessively anxious to know what had happened. Fixing his credulous eyes on the bandaged head, he asked, trembling slightly:

"And did it—did it knock you down?"

"Come! am I the sort of man to be knocked down by a ghost?" protested Bunter in a little stronger tone. "Don't you remember what you said yourself the other night? Better men than me—— Ha! you'll have to look a long time before you find a better man for a mate of your ship."

Captain Johns pointed a solemn finger at Bunter's bedplace.

"You've been terrified," he said. "That's what's the matter. You've been terrified. Why, even the man at the wheel was scared, though he couldn't see anything. He *felt* the supernatural. You are punished for your incredulity, Mr. Bunter. You were terrified."

"And suppose I was," said Bunter. "Do you know what I had seen? Can you conceive the sort of ghost that would haunt a man like me? Do you think it was a ladyish, afternoon call, another-cup-of-tea-please apparition that visits your Professor Cranks and that journalist chap you are always talking about? No; I can't tell you what it was like. Every man has his own ghosts. You couldn't conceive . . . ."

Bunter stopped, out of breath; and Captain Johns remarked, with the glow of inward satisfaction reflected in his tone:

"I've always thought you were the sort of man that was ready for anything; from pitch-and-toss to wilful murder, as the saying goes. Well, well! So you were terrified."

"I stepped back," said Bunter, curtly. "I don't remember anything else."

"The man at the wheel told me you went backwards as if something had hit you."

"It was a sort of inward blow," explained Bunter. "Something too deep for you, Captain Johns, to understand. Your life and mine haven't been the same. Aren't you satisfied to see me converted?"

"And you can't tell me any more?" asked Captain Johns, anxiously.

"No, I can't. I wouldn't. It would be no use if I did. That sort of experience must be gone through. Say I am being punished. Well, I take my punishment, but talk of it I won't."

"Very well," said Captain Johns; "you won't. But, mind, I can draw my own conclusions from that."

"Draw what you like; but be careful what you say, sir. You don't terrify me. *You* aren't a ghost."

"One word. Has it any connection with what you said to me on that last night, when we had a talk together on spiritualism?"

Bunter looked weary and puzzled.

"What did I say?"

"You told me that I couldn't know what a man like you was capable of."

"Yes, yes. Enough!"

"Very good. I am fixed, then," remarked Captain Johns. "All I say is that I am jolly glad not to be you, though I would have given almost anything for the privilege of personal communication with the world of spirits. Yes, sir, but not in that way."

Poor Bunter moaned pitifully.

"It has made me feel twenty years older."

Captain Johns retired quietly. He was delighted to observe this overbearing ruffian humbled to the dust by the moralizing agency of the spirits. The whole occurrence was a source of pride and gratification; and he began to feel a sort of regard for his chief mate.

It is true that in further interviews Bunter showed himself very mild and deferential. He seemed to cling to his captain for spiritual protection. He used to send for him, and say, "I feel so nervous," and Captain Johns would stay patiently for hours in the hot little cabin, and feel proud of the call.

For Mr. Bunter was ill, and could not leave his berth for a good many days. He became a convinced spiritualist, not enthusiastically—that could hardly have been expected from him—but in a grim, unshakable way. He could not be called exactly friendly to the disembodied inhabitants of our globe, as Captain Johns was. But he was now a firm, if gloomy, recruit of spiritualism.

One afternoon, as the ship was already well to the north in the Gulf of Bengal, the steward knocked at the door of the captain's cabin, and said, without opening it:

"The mate asks if you could spare him a moment, sir. He seems to be in a state in there."

Captain Johns jumped up from the couch at once.

"Yes. Tell him I am coming."

He thought: Could it be possible there had been another spiritual manifestation—in the daytime, too!

He revelled in the hope. It was not exactly that, however. Still, Bunter, whom he saw sitting collapsed in a chair—he had been up for several days, but not on deck as yet—poor Bunter had something startling enough to communicate. His hands covered his face. His legs were stretched straight out, dismally.

"What's the news now?" croaked Captain Johns, not unkindly, because in truth it always pleased him to see Bunter—as he expressed it—tamed.

"News!" exclaimed the crushed sceptic through his hands. "Ay, news enough, Captain Johns. Who

will be able to deny the awfulness, the genuineness?
Another man would have dropped dead. You want
to know what I had seen. All I can tell you is that
since I've seen it my hair is turning white."

Bunter detached his hands from his face, and they
hung on each side of his chair as if dead. He looked
broken in the dusky cabin.

"You don't say!" stammered out Captain Johns.
"Turned white! Hold on a bit! I'll light the lamp!"

When the lamp was lit, the startling phenomenon
could be seen plainly enough. As if the dread, the
horror, the anguish of the supernatural were being
exhaled through the pores of his skin, a sort of silvery
mist seemed to cling to the cheeks and the head of
the mate. His short beard, his cropped hair, were
growing, not black, but gray—almost white.

When Mr. Bunter, thin-faced and shaky, came on
deck for duty, he was clean-shaven, and his head was
white. The hands were awe-struck. "Another man,"
they whispered to each other. It was generally and
mysteriously agreed that the mate had "seen something," with the exception of the man at the wheel at
the time, who maintained that the mate was "struck
by something."

This distinction hardly amounted to a difference.
On the other hand, everybody admitted that, after he
picked up his strength a bit, he seemed even smarter in
his movements than before.

One day in Calcutta, Captain Johns, pointing out to a
visitor his white-headed chief mate standing by the
main-hatch, was heard to say oracularly:

"That man's in the prime of life."

Of course, while Bunter was away, I called regularly
on Mrs. Bunter every Saturday, just to see whether
she had any use for my services. It was understood

E

I would do that. She had just his half-pay to live on—it amounted to about a pound a week. She had taken one room in a quiet little square in the East End.

And this was affluence to what I had heard that the couple were reduced to for a time after Bunter had to give up the Western Ocean trade—he used to go as mate of all sorts of hard packets after he lost his ship and his luck together—it was affluence to that time when Bunter would start at seven o'clock in the morning with but a glass of hot water and a crust of dry bread. It won't stand thinking about, especially for those who know Mrs. Bunter. I had seen something of them too, at that time; and it just makes me shudder to remember what that born lady had to put up with. Enough!

Dear Mrs. Bunter used to worry a good deal after the *Sapphire* left for Calcutta. She would say to me: "It must be so awful for poor Winston"—Winston is Bunter's name—and I tried to comfort her the best I could. Afterwards, she got some small children to teach in a family, and was half the day with them, and the occupation was good for her.

In the very first letter she had from Calcutta, Bunter told her he had had a fall down the poop-ladder, and cut his head, but no bones broken, thank God. That was all. Of course, she had other letters from him, but that vagabond Bunter never gave me a scratch of the pen the solid eleven months. I supposed, naturally, that everything was going on all right. Who could imagine what was happening?

Then one day dear Mrs. Bunter got a letter from a legal firm in the City, advising her that her uncle was dead—her old curmudgeon of an uncle—a retired stock-broker, a heartless, petrified antiquity that had lasted on and on. He was nearly ninety, I believe; and if I

were to meet his venerable ghost this minute, I would
try to take him by the throat and strangle him.

The old beast would never forgive his niece for marrying Bunter; and years afterwards, when people made a
point of letting him know that she was in London,
pretty nearly starving at forty years of age, he only
said: "Serve the little fool right!" I believe he meant
her to starve. And, lo and behold, the old cannibal
died intestate, with no other relatives but that very
identical little fool. The Bunters were wealthy people
now.

Of course, Mrs. Bunter wept as if her heart would
break. In any other woman it would have been mere
hypocrisy. Naturally, too, she wanted to cable the
news to her Winston in Calcutta, but I showed her,
Gazette in hand, that the ship was on the homeward-
bound list for more than a week already. So we sat
down to wait, and talked meantime of dear old Winston
every day. There were just one hundred such days
before the Sapphire got reported "All well" in the chops
of the Channel by an incoming mailboat.

"I am going to Dunkirk to meet him," says she.
The Sapphire had a cargo of jute for Dunkirk. Of
course, I had to escort the dear lady in the quality of
her "ingenious friend." She calls me "our ingenious
friend" to this day; and I've observed some people—
strangers—looking hard at me, for the signs of the
ingenuity, I suppose.

After settling Mrs. Bunter in a good hotel in Dunkirk, I walked down to the docks—late afternoon it
was—and what was my surprise to see the ship actually
fast alongside. Either Johns or Bunter, or both, must
have been driving her hard up Channel. Anyway,
she had been in since the day before last, and her crew
was already paid off. I met two of her apprenticed

boys going off home on leave with their dunnage on a Frenchman's barrow, as happy as larks, and I asked them if the mate was on board.

"There he is, on the quay, looking at the moorings," says one of the youngsters as he skipped past me.

You may imagine the shock to my feelings when I beheld his white head. I could only manage to tell him that his wife was at an hotel in town. He left me at once, to go and get his hat on board. I was mightily surprised by the smartness of his movements as he hurried up the gangway.

Whereas the black mate struck people as deliberate, and strangely stately in his gait for a man in the prime of life, this white-headed chap seemed the most wonderfully alert of old men. I don't suppose Bunter was any quicker on his pins than before. It was the colour of the hair that made all the difference in one's judgment.

The same with his eyes. Those eyes, that looked at you so steely, so fierce, and so fascinating out of a bush of a buccaneer's black hair, now had an innocent, almost boyish expression in their good-humoured brightness under those white eyebrows.

I led him without any delay into Mrs. Bunter's private sitting-room. After she had dropped a tear over the late cannibal, given a hug to her Winston, and told him that he must grow his moustache again, the dear lady tucked her feet upon the sofa, and I got out of Bunter's way.

He started at once to pace the room, waving his long arms. He worked himself into a regular frenzy, and tore Johns limb from limb many times over that evening.

"Fell down? Of course I fell down, by slipping backwards on that fool's patent brass plates. 'Pon my word, I had been walking that poop in charge of the

ship, and I didn't know whether I was in the Indian
Ocean or in the moon. I was crazy. My head spun
round and round with sheer worry. I had made my
last application of your chemist's wonderful stuff."
(This to me.) "All the store of bottles you gave me
got smashed when those drawers fell out in the last gale.
I had been getting some dry things to change, when I
heard the cry: 'All hands on deck!' and made one jump
of it, without even pushing them in properly. Ass!
When I came back and saw the broken glass and the
mess, I felt ready to faint.

"No; look here—deception is bad; but not to be able
to keep it up after one has been forced into it. You
know that since I've been squeezed out of the Western
Ocean packets by younger men, just on account of my
grizzled muzzle—you know how much chance I had to
ever get a ship. And not a soul to turn to. We have
been a lonely couple, we two—she threw away everything for me—and to see her want a piece of dry
bread——"

He banged with his fist fit to split the Frenchman's
table in two.

"I would have turned a sanguinary pirate for her,
let alone cheating my way into a berth by dyeing my
hair. So when you came to me with your chemist's
wonderful stuff——"

He checked himself.

"By the way, that fellow's got a fortune when he
likes to pick it up. It is a wonderful stuff—you tell
him salt water can do nothing to it. It stays on as long
as your hair will."

"All right," I said. "Go on."

Thereupon he went for Johns again with a fury that
frightened his wife, and made me laugh till I cried.

"Just you try to think what it would have meant to

be at the mercy of the meanest creature that ever commanded a ship! Just fancy what a life that crawling Johns would have led me! And I knew that in a week or so the white hair would begin to show. And the crew. Did you ever think of that? To be shown up as a low fraud before all hands. What a life for me till we got to Calcutta! And once there—kicked out, of course. Half-pay stopped. Annie here alone without a penny—starving; and I on the other side of the earth, ditto. You see?

"I thought of shaving twice a day. But could I shave my head, too? No way—no way at all. Unless I dropped Johns overboard; and even then——
Do you wonder now that with all these things boiling in my head I didn't know where I was putting down my foot that night? I just felt myself falling—then crash, and all dark.

"When I came to myself that bang on the head seemed to have steadied my wits somehow. I was so sick of everything that for two days I wouldn't speak to anyone. They thought it was a slight concussion of the brain. Then the idea dawned upon me as I was looking at that ghost-ridden, wretched fool. 'Ah, you love ghosts,' I thought. 'Well, you shall have something from beyond the grave.'

"I didn't even trouble to invent a story. I couldn't imagine a ghost if I wanted to. I wasn't fit to lie connectedly if I had tried. I just bulled him on to it. Do you know, he got, quite by himself, a notion that at some time or other I had done somebody to death in some way, and that——"

"Oh, the horrible man!" cried Mrs. Bunter from the sofa. There was a silence.

"And didn't he bore my head off on the home passage!" began Bunter again in a weary voice. "H loved me. He was proud of me. I was converted. I had had a manifestation. Do you know what he was after? He wanted me and him 'to make a *seance*,' in his own words, and to try to call up that ghost (the one that had turned my hair white—the ghost of my supposed victim), and, as he said, talk it over with him —the ghost—in a friendly way.

"'Or else, Bunter,' he says, 'you may get another manifestation when you least expect it, and tumble overboard perhaps, or something. You ain't really safe till we pacify the spirit-world in some way.'

"Can you conceive a lunatic like that? No—say?"

I said nothing. But Mrs. Bunter did, in a very decided tone.

"Winston, I don't want you to go on board that ship again any more."

"My dear," says he, "I have all my things on board yet."

"You don't want the things. Don't go near that ship at all."

He stood still; then, dropping his eyes with a faint smile, said slowly, in a dreamy voice:

"The haunted ship."

"And your last," I added.

We carried him off, as he stood, by the night train. He was very quiet; but crossing the Channel, as we two had a smoke on deck, he turned to me suddenly, and, grinding his teeth, whispered:

"He'll never know how near he was being dropped overboard!"

He meant Captain Johns. I said nothing.

But Captain Johns, I understand, made a great to-do about the disappearance of his chief mate. He set the French police scouring the country for the body. In the end, I fancy he got word from his owners' office to drop all this fuss—that it was all right. I don't suppose he ever understood anything of that mysterious occurrence.

To this day he tries at times (he's retired now, and his conversation is not very coherent)—he tries to tell the story of a black mate he once had, "a murderous, gentlemanly ruffian," with raven-black hair which turned white all at once in consequence of a manifestation from beyond the grave." An avenging apparition. What with reference to black and white hair, to poop-ladders, and to his own feelings and views, it is difficult to make head or tail of it. If his sister (she's very vigorous still) should be present she cuts all this short—peremptorily:

"Don't you mind what he says. He's got devils on the brain."

THE END

LAST ESSAYS

I wonder who say they you *to tell.*
...... have been in ironmonger or
with a ...... his trade ...... a new opening for

He must have been an ironmonger
trying to ...... amulet for his wares.
And to what ...... audience. Personally
I would have been afraid to tell
it to ...... — Meanings that ...... is ...... to
which is ...... the ...... to
swallow anything in the way of a
yarn.

THE LAST WORDS THAT CONRAD WROTE

INTRODUCTION

MOST of the contents of this volume were written
subsequent to the publication of "Notes on Life and
Letters" in 1921, and these two books together may be
said to contain practically all Conrad's miscellaneous
writings. There are, it is true, a few short prefaces and
some interesting letters to newspapers which might have
been included here, but they are of no particular importance, and the twenty separate pieces gathered between these covers are indeed the last essays of Joseph
Conrad. But there remains a chance that some of his
early essays and reviews may still rest undiscovered in
the files of old newspapers and weeklies. Conrad had
a very uncertain memory for his own work, and I recall
that when the material for "Notes on Life and Letters"
was being collected, he was frequently quite vague as
to what he had written and where it had appeared.
In proof of this, it may be mentioned that the essay
entitled "John Galsworthy" in this volume was omitted from the previous one only through Conrad's forget-
fulness of its existence. Therefore, as I say, discoveries
may yet be made.

In the latter years of his life Conrad occasionally
found relief from the toil and exhaustion of more creative work in the writing of reminiscent essays, and some
of these rank, decidedly, among his finest efforts in this
direction. "Last Essays" is just as remarkable a book
as "Notes on Life and Letters"; it contains passages
of extraordinary charm, serenity, and eloquence. And

particular care has been taken to avoid any aspect of absolute completeness, as though a dead author's desk had been ransacked for every fragment: all the articles included in this volume have been included for very definite reasons. Nothing has been printed merely for the purpose of adding to the bulk.

For some time Conrad had had the idea of writing a pendent volume to "The Mirror of the Sea," and the unfinished article, "Legends," on which he was at work the day before he died, was, he told me, to have formed part of such a book. And I suspect that "The *Torrens*," "Christmas Day at Sea," "Ocean Travel," "Outside Literature," and part, at least, of "Geography and Some Explorers," would also have been incorporated in this book, and therefore I have placed them all together at the beginning of the volume. They form, as it were, the shadowy nucleus of a projected work.

"Geography and Some Explorers," the second longest essay in this collection, was written as a general introduction to a serial work called "Countries of the World." It appeared as "The Romance of Travel" in the first number, February, 1924, and was reprinted under its proper title in *The National Geographic Magazine*, March, 1924. In this fascinating essay, Conrad, after discussing the feats of some of the early navigators and explorers, gives a memorable account of a passage he made in 1888 (when in command of the *Otago*) through the Torres Straits on a voyage from Sydney to Mauritius.

"The *Torrens*: A Personal Tribute," was published in *The Blue Peter*, October, 1923. In the early 'nineties Conrad had been chief officer of this ship—he joined her on November 2, 1891, and left her on October 15, 1893—and he made two journeys from England to Australia and back in that capacity. For her he always retained a warm affection, and when, in the September *Blue Peter* of 1923, there was issued a coloured illustration of the *Torrens*, he willingly consented to give a personal remembrance of her in the next number. The last words, in which he describes her end upon the shores of the Mediterranean, possess a rare and pensive beauty, which I recover in the following paragraph:

"But in the end her body of iron and wood, so fair to look upon, had to be broken up—I hope with fitting reverence; and as I sit here, thirty years, almost to a day, since I last set eyes on her, I love to think that her perfect form found a merciful end on the shores of the Sunlit Sea of my boyhood's dreams, and that her fine spirit has returned to dwell in the regions of the great winds, the inspirers and companions of her swift, renowned, sea-tossed life which I, too, have been permitted to share for a little while."

"Christmas Day at Sea" was published in the London *Daily Mail* on December 24, 1923. It was concerned largely with an episode on one Christmas Day during Conrad's first voyage to Australia in the *Duke of Sutherland* in 1879, where he served as an A. B.

"Ocean Travel" made its first appearance in the London *Evening News* of May 15, 1923, where it was named "My Hotel in Mid-Atlantic." It was written during Conrad's voyage to America in the *Tuscania* in the spring of that year, and was posted to me the moment he arrived in New York. It compares the old and the new life at sea, and, needless to say, the vote of affection is given for the old.

"Outside Literature," a short essay dealing with the subject of notices to mariners, appeared under the title "Notices to Mariners" in the *Manchester Guardian* of December 4, 1922, and under its proper title in the American *Bookman* of February, 1923.

"Legends," as I have mentioned, was the last article Conrad ever wrote; it was left unfinished upon his desk. It tells, with a strain of melancholy, of the breed of seamen who have disappeared with the disappearance of sailing ships, and was printed, less than a fortnight after Conrad's death, in the London *Daily Mail* of August 15, 1924.

Next follow two essays which have the war at sea as background. "The Unlighted Coast" recalls Conrad's experiences in the North Sea during his ten-days' cruise in the *Ready* in 1917—a full account of this cruise is to be found in Captain Sutherland's "At Sea with Joseph Conrad"—and was written for the Admiralty. For some reason or other they never used it and it first saw the light in the London *Times* of August 18, 1925.

"The Dover Patrol," written at the request of the late Lord Northcliffe, was published in the London *Times* of July 27, 1921, the day on which the Prince of Wales unveiled the Dover Patrol Memorial. It is a glowing tribute to "the physical endurance, the inborn seamanship, the matter-of-fact, industrious, indefatigable enthusiasm" of the men who guarded unsleepingly and at extreme hazard the entrance to the Channel.

The "Memorandum on the Scheme for Fitting Out a Sailing Ship" is here first printed. Written in 1919 for the Holt Steamship Company, who had proposed to fit out a sailing ship for the training of boys destined for the Mercantile Marine, it is an example of Conrad's intense and practical interest in such subjects. It is exactly what it purports to be—a memorandum, precise, technical, full of his accumulated experience and long-pondered ideas. Nothing came of the scheme: as Mr. Lawrence Holt wrote to me, it was "abandoned owing to the depression of trade which set in soon after my conversation with Mr. Conrad." The document from then to now has been in Mr. Holt's possession, and cordial thanks are due to him for his permission to use it here.

"The Loss of the *Dalgonar*" is a further example of Conrad's interest in questions of seamanship. Indeed, I print it solely for that reason, because, in itself, it but refers to the contents of an article from another pen. It appeared, as a letter to the editor, in the London *Mercury* of December, 1921, and was called forth by a paper in the September issue entitled "A True Story: Log and Record of the Wreck of the Ship *Dalgonar* of Liverpool, bound from Callao to Taltal." This paper described the wreck of the barque *Loire*, which happened in October, 1913; and Conrad's letter, while correcting some obvious mistakes in the narrative as printed, is a testimony to the gallantry and efficiency of the officers and crew.

The essay called "Travel" was written, I am proud to think, out of friendship for myself, and formed the preface to a book by me, "Into the East: Notes on Burma and Malaya," 1923. The effort to finish "The Rover" held up the writing of this preface for about a year, but it seems to me that in its evocation of the great travellers of old and of times that have gone for ever it reaches the highest beauty and distinction. Let me quote one paragraph:

"And those things, which stand as if imperishable in the pages of old books of travel, are all blown away; have vanished as utterly as the smoke of the travellers' camp fires in the icy night air of the Gobi Desert, as the smell of incense burned in the temples of strange gods, as the voices of Asiatic statesmen speculating with the cruel wisdom of past ages on matters of peace and war."

"Stephen Crane," the longest and most elaborate essay in the book, was written as an introduction to

Mr. Thomas Beer's "Stephen Crane, a Study in American Letters," 1923. Conrad, as is generally known, was a close friend of Crane during the last years of that meteoric life, when Crane was frequently a neighbour of his in southern England. In all, he wrote three essays on Crane and his work. One appeared in "Notes on Life and Letters," two are printed in this volume, and all breathe a spirit of affectionate admiration. This essay is a study in biographical sidelights and is undoubtedly the most personal and the most delightful of all reminiscences of Crane.

The short essay, "His War Book," which follows, was composed specifically as a preface to a new edition of Crane's best-known work, "The Red Badge of Courage" —the new edition came out at last in 1925—and it gives clear indication of Conrad's feeling for the artist who could observe so truly and create with such economy.

"John Galsworthy," as I have said, was only accidentally omitted from the previous volume of Conrad's essays. It was composed as a review of "A Man of Property," contained in a wider study of the author, and was published in the London *Outlook* of March 31, 1906, under the title of "A Middle Class Family." A few years before he died, Conrad rectified, as far as he could, his oversight by privately printing about fifty copies of this essay, and he would certainly have included it in any future volume of essays.

The next piece, "A Glance at Two Books," dealing with Galsworthy's "The Island Pharisees" and Hudson's "Green Mansions," dates from even earlier and was done in 1904. Written obviously in answer to an editorial request, it was, for reasons unknown, never used, and the typescript, being found among Conrad's papers, was first printed in *T. P.'s and Cassell's Weekly* of August 1, 1925.

A "Preface to his Shorter Tales" was written at the instigation of his American publishers to introduce "The Shorter Tales of Joseph Conrad," and the essay, like the selection, has never appeared in England. It was one of his last completed pieces—the volume was issued after his death in 1924—and it throws a reminiscent glance upon the ideas that animated his work and upon his writing life.

The little note, "Cookery," charming in its playful fancy, was a send-off to his wife's book, "A Handbook of Cookery for a Small House," 1922. I include it here for the sake of its association and for the unique quality of its tone.

The next two pieces, both of them letters, give glimpses of Conrad's abiding interest in international questions and the affairs of Europe. He was always a student of foreign politics, a student fortified by an impressive historical sense and by a great knowledge of continental problems throughout the centuries, and these two letters, with their combined eloquence and hold upon reality, throw light upon an aspect of Conrad's mind of which few people are aware.

The first letter, an appeal for a free Constantinople under the protection of the Powers, was published in the London *Times* of November 7, 1912, when the Balkan States were at war with Turkey and their armies already within striking distance of her capital.

The second letter, written evidently a few days later to an untraceable correspondent—a typescript only was found—who had criticized his printed observations, is an amplification of the previous letter.

Finally comes "The Congo Diary," a reprint of the diary kept by Conrad in the Congo in 1890, which was first published in *The Blue Peter*, October, 1925, and then in *The Yale Review*, January, 1926. This diary calls for its own introduction and a series of explanatory notes, and these will be found with it at the end of the book.

Here, then, are the twenty pieces which compose this volume of "Last Essays." They show as clearly as did the contents of "Notes on Life and Letters" the rich diversity of Conrad's mind, his powers of cogent argument, of fond memory, and of noble expression. His mastery over his chosen material never flagged and these essays are a last witness to his consummate gifts.

RICHARD CURLE.

LAST ESSAYS

GEOGRAPHY AND SOME EXPLORERS

It is safe to say that for the majority of mankind
the superiority of geography over geometry lies in the
appeal of its figures. It may be an effect of the incorrigible frivolity inherent in human nature, but most
of us will agree that a map is more fascinating to look
at than a figure in a treatise on conic sections—at any
rate for the simple minds which are all the equipment
of the majority of the dwellers on this earth.

No doubt a trigonometrical survey may be a romantic
undertaking, striding over deserts and leaping over
valleys never before trodden by the foot of civilized
man; but its accurate operations can never have for us
the fascination of the first hazardous steps of a venture-
some, often lonely, explorer jotting down by the light
of his camp fire the thoughts, the impressions, and the
toil of his day.

For a long time yet a few suggestive words grappling
with things seen will have the advantage over a long
array of precise, no doubt interesting, and even profit-
able figures. The earth is a stage, and though it may
be an advantage, even to the right comprehension of the
play, to know its exact configuration, it is the drama of
human endeavour that will be the thing, with a ruling
passion expressed by outward action marching perhaps
blindly to success or failure, which themselves are often
undistinguishable from each other at first.

Of all the sciences, geography finds its origin in action, and what is more, in adventurous action of the kind that appeals to sedentary people who like to dream of arduous adventure in the manner of prisoners dreaming behind bars of all the hardships and hazards of liberty dear to the heart of man.

Descriptive geography, like any other kind of science, has been built on the experience of certain phenomena and on experiments prompted by that unappeasable curiosity of men which their intelligence has elevated into a quite respectable passion for acquiring knowledge. Like other sciences it has fought its way to truth through a long series of errors. It has suffered from the love of the marvellous, from our credulity, from rash and unwarrantable assumptions, from the play of unbridled fancy.

Geography had its phase of circumstantially extravagant speculation which had nothing to do with the pursuit of truth, but has given us a curious glimpse of the mediæval mind playing in its ponderous childish way with the problems of our earth's shape, its size, its character, its products, its inhabitants. Cartography was almost as pictorial then as are some modern newspapers. It crowded its maps with pictures of strange pageants, strange trees, strange beasts, drawn with amazing precision in the midst of theoretically conceived continents. It delineated imaginary kingdoms of Monomotapa and of Prester John, the regions infested by lions or haunted by unicorns, inhabited by men with reversed feet, or eyes in the middle of their breasts.

All this might have been amusing if the mediæval gravity in the absurd had not been in itself a wearisome thing. But what of that! Has not the key science of modern chemistry passed through its dishonest phase of Alchemy (a portentous development of the confidence trick), and our knowledge of the starry sky been arrived at through the superstitious idealism of Astrology looking for men's fate in the depths of the infinite? Mere megalomania on a colossal scale. Yet, solemn fooling for solemn fooling of the scientific order, I prefer the kind that does not lay itself out to thrive on the fears and the cupidities of men.

From that point of view geography is the most blameless of sciences. Its fabulous phase never aimed at cheating simple mortals (who are a multitude) out of their peace of mind or their money. At the most it has enticed some of them away from their homes; to death may be, now and then to a little disputed glory, not seldom to contumely, never to high fortune. The greatest of them all, who has presented modern geography with a new world to work upon, was at one time loaded with chains and thrown into prison. Columbus remains a pathetic figure, not a sufferer in the cause of geography, but a victim of the imperfections of jealous human hearts, accepting his fate with resignation. Among explorers he appears lofty in his troubles and like a man of a kingly nature. His contribution to the knowledge of the earth was certainly royal. And if the discovery of America was the occasion of the greatest outburst of reckless cruelty and greed known to history we may say this at least for it, that the gold of Mexico and Peru, unlike the gold of alchemists, was really there, palpable, yet, as ever, the most elusive of the Fata Morgana that lure men away from their homes, as a moment of reflection will convince any one. For nothing is more certain than that there will never be enough gold to go round, as the Conquistadores found out by experience.

I suppose it is not very charitable of me, but I must

say that to this day I feel a malicious pleasure at the many disappointments of those pertinacious searchers for El Dorado who climbed mountains, pushed through forests, swam rivers, floundered in bogs, without giving a single thought to the science of geography. Not for them the serene joys of scientific research, but infinite toil, in hunger, thirst, sickness, battle; with broken heads, unseemly squabbles, and empty pockets in the end. I cannot help thinking it served them right. It is an ugly tale, which has not much to do with the service of geography. The geographical knowledge of our day is of the kind that would have been beyond the conception of the hardy followers of Cortés and Pizarro; and of that most estimable of Conquerors who was called Cabeza de Vaca, who was high-minded and dealt humanely with the heathen nations whose territories he traversed in search of one more El Dorado. It is said they loved him greatly, but now the very memory of those nations is gone from the earth, while their territories, which they could not take with them, are being traversed many times every twenty-four hours by the trains of the Southern Pacific railroad.

The discovery of the New World marks the end of the fabulous geography, and it must be owned that the history of the Conquest contains at least one great moment—I mean a geographically great moment— when Vasco Núñez de Balboa, while crossing the Isthmus of Panama, set his eyes for the first time upon the ocean, the immensity of which he did not suspect, and which in his elation he named the Pacific. It is anything but that; but the privileged Conquistador cannot be blamed for surrendering to his first impression.

The Gulf of Panama, which is what he really saw with that first glance, is one of the calmest spots on the waters of the globe. Too calm. The old navigators dreaded it as a dangerous region where one might be caught and lie becalmed for weeks with one's crew dying slowly of thirst under a cloudless sky. The worst of fates, this, to feel yourself die in a long and helpless agony. How much preferable a region of storms where man and ship can at least put up a fight and remain defiant almost to the last.

I must not be understood to mean that a tempest at sea is a delightful experience, but I would rather face the fiercest tempest than a gulf pacific even to deadliness, a prison-house for incautious caravels and a place of torture for their crews. But Balboa was charmed with its serene aspect. He did not know where he was. He probably thought himself within a stone's throw, as it were, of the Indies and Cathay. Or did he perhaps, like a man touched with grace, have a moment of exalted vision, the awed feeling that what he was looking at was an abyss of waters comparable in its extent to the view of the unfathomable firmament, and sown all over with groups of islands resembling the constellations of the sky?

But whatever spiritual glimpse of the truth he might have had, Balboa could not possibly know that this great moment of his life had added suddenly thousands of miles to the circumference of the globe, had opened an immense theatre for the human drama of adventure and exploration, a field for the missionary labours of, mainly, Protestant churches, and spread an enormous canvas on which armchair geographers could paint the most fanciful variants of their pet theory of a great southern continent.

I will not quarrel with the post-Columbian cartographers for their wild but, upon the whole, interesting inventions. The provocation to let one's self go was

considerable. Geography militant, which had succeeded the geography fabulous, did not seem able
to accept the idea that there was much more water
than land on this globe. Nothing could satisfy their
sense of the fitness of things but an enormous extent
of solid earth which they placed in that region of the
South where, as a matter of fact, the great white-crested
seas of stormy latitudes will be free to chase each other
all round the globe to the end of time. I suppose
their landsmen's temperament stood in the way of their
recognition that the world of geography, so far as the
apportioning of space goes, seems to have been planned
mostly for the convenience of fishes.

What is surprising to me is that the seamen of the
time should have really believed that the large continents to the north of the Equator demanded, as a
matter of good art or else of sound science, to be
balanced by corresponding masses of land in the
southern hemisphere. They were simple souls. The
chorus of armchair people all singing the same tune
made them blind to the many plain signs of a great open
sea. Every bit of coast-line discovered, every mountain-
top glimpsed in the distance, had to be dragged loyally
into the scheme of the Terra Australis Incognita.

Even Tasman, the best seaman of them all before
James Cook, the most accomplished of seventeenth-
century explorers and navigators that went forth to
settle the geography of the Pacific—even Tasman,
after coming unexpectedly upon the North Island of
New Zealand, and lingering long enough there to
chart roughly a bit of the coast and lose a boat's crew
in a sudden affray with the Maoris, seemed to take it
for granted that this was the western limit of an
enormous continent extending away towards the point
of South America.

Mighty is the power of a theory, especially if based on such a common-sense notion as the balance of continents. And it must be remembered that it is difficult for us now to realize not only the navigational dangers of unknown seas, but the awful geographical incertitudes of the first explorers in that new world of waters.

Tasman's journal, which was published not so very long ago, gives us some idea of their perplexing difficulties. The early navigators had no means of ascertaining their exact position on the globe. They could calculate their latitude, but the problem of longitude was a matter which bewildered their minds and often falsified their judgment. It had to be a matter of pure guesswork. Tasman and his officers, when they met on board the *Heemskirk*, anchored in Murderers' Bay, to consider their further course in the light of their instructions, did not know where any of the problematic places named in their instructions were, neither did they know where they themselves were.

Tasman might have sailed north or east, but in the end he decided to sail between the two, and, circling about, returned to Batavia, where he was received coldly by his employers, the honourable governor-general and the council in Batavia. Their final judgment was that Abel Tasman was a skilful navigator, but that he had shown himself "remiss" in his investigations, and that he had been guilty of leaving certain problems unsolved.

We are told that Tasman did not expect this armchair criticism; and indeed, even now, it seems surprising to an unprejudiced mind. It was the voyage during which, among other things, Tasman discovered the island by which his name lives on the charts, took first contact with New Zealand (which was not seen again till 130 years afterwards), sailed over many thousands of miles of uncharted seas, bringing back with him a journal which was of much value afterwards for his exploring successors.

It may be he was hurt by the verdict of the honourable council, but he does not seem to have been cast down by it, for it appears that shortly afterwards he asked for a rise of salary—and, what is still more significant, he got it. He was obviously a valuable servant, but I am sorry to say that his character as a man was not of the kind to cause governors and councils to treat him with particular consideration. Except in professional achievement he is not comparable to Captain Cook, a humble son of the soil like himself, but a modest man of genius, the familiar associate of the most learned in the land, medallist of the Royal Society, and a captain in the Royal Navy.

But there was a taint of an unscrupulous adventurer in Tasman. It is certain that at various times his patron, the Governor Anthony van Diemen, and the honourable council in Batavia, had employed him in some shady transactions of their own, connected with the Japan trade. There is also no doubt that once he had, on his own responsibility, kidnapped an influential Chinaman who stood in the way of some business negotiation Tasman was conducting with the Sultan of Achin.

The Chinaman may have been a worthless person, but one wonders what happened to him in the end; and, in any case, the proceeding is open to criticism. Then in his old age he got into some disreputable scrape which caused the congregation with which he worshipped to ask him to resign his membership. Even the honourable council was startled, and dismissed him from his employment, though characteristically enough not actually from their service. This action of the council fixes the character of the man better than any scandalous story. He was valuable, but compromising.

All these regrettable details came to my knowledge quite recently in a very amusing and interesting book, but I must confess that my early admiration for Tasman as one of the early fathers of militant geography has not been affected very much by it. Remiss or not, he had in the course of his voyages mapped 8,000 miles of an island which by common consent is called now a continent, a geologically very old continent indeed, but which is now the home of a very young commonwealth with all the possibilities of material and intellectual splendour still hidden in its future.

I like to think that in that portion of the Elysian Fields set apart for great navigators, James Cook would not refuse to acknowledge the civilities of Abel Tasman, a fellow seaman who had first reported the existence of New Zealand in the perplexed, bewildered way of those times, 130 years before Captain Cook on his second voyage laid for ever the ghost of the Terra Australis Incognita and added New Zealand to the scientific domain of the geography triumphant of our day.

No shade of remissness nor doubtful motive rests upon the achievements of Captain Cook, who came out of a labourer's cottage to take his place at the head of the masters of maritime exploration who worked at the great geographical problem of the Pacific. *Endeavour* was the name of the ship which carried him on his first voyage, and it was also the watchword of his professional life. *Resolution* was the name of the ship he commanded himself on his second expedition, and it was the determining quality of his soul. I will not say that it was the greatest, because he had all the other manly qualities of a great man.

The voyages of the early explorers were prompted by an acquisitive spirit, the idea of lucre in some form, the desire of trade or the desire of loot, disguised in more or less fine words. But Cook's three voyages are free from any taint of that sort. His aims needed no disguise. They were scientific. His deeds speak for themselves with the masterly simplicity of a hard-won success. In that respect he seems to belong to the single-minded explorers of the nineteenth century, the late fathers of militant geography whose only object was the search for truth. Geography is a science of facts, and they devoted themselves to the discovery of facts in the configuration and features of the main continents.

It was the century of landsmen investigators. In saying this I do not forget the polar explorers, whose aims were certainly as pure as the air of those high latitudes where not a few of them laid down their lives for the advancement of geography. Seamen, men of science, it is difficult to speak of them without admirative emotion. The dominating figure among the seamen explorers of the first half of the nineteenth century is that of another good man, Sir John Franklin, whose fame rests not only on the extent of his discoveries, but on professional prestige and high personal character. This great navigator, who never returned home, served geography even in his death. The persistent efforts extending over ten years to ascertain his fate advanced greatly our knowledge of the polar regions.

As gradually revealed to the world this fate appeared the more tragic in this, that for the first two years the way of the *Erebus* and *Terror* expedition seemed to be the way to the desired and important success, while in truth it was all the time the way of death, the end of the darkest drama perhaps played behind the curtain of Arctic mystery.

The last words unveiling the mystery of the *Erebus* and *Terror* expedition were brought home and disclosed to the world by Sir Leopold McClintock, in his book, "The Voyage of the *Fox* in the Arctic Seas." It is a little book, but it records with manly simplicity the tragic ending of a great tale. It so happened that I was born in the year of its publication. Therefore, I may be excused for not getting hold of it till ten years afterwards. I can only account for it falling into my hands by the fact that the fate of Sir John Franklin was a matter of European interest, and that Sir Leopold McClintock's book was translated, I believe, into every language of the white races.

My copy was probably in French. But I have read the work many times since. I have now on my shelves a copy of a popular edition got up exactly as I remember my first one. It contains the touching facsimile of the printed form filled in with a summary record of the two ships' work, the name of "Sir John Franklin commanding the expedition" written in ink, and the pathetic underlined entry "All well." It was found by Sir Leopold McClintock under a cairn and it is dated just a year before the two ships had to be abandoned in their deadly ice-trap, and their crews' long and desperate struggle for life began.

There could hardly have been imagined a better book for letting in the breath of the stern romance of polar exploration into the existence of a boy whose knowledge of the poles of the earth had been till then of an abstract formal kind as mere imaginary ends of the imaginary

axis upon which the earth turns. The great spirit of
the realities of the story sent me off on the romantic
explorations of my inner self; to the discovery of the
taste of poring over maps; and revealed to me the
existence of a latent devotion to geography which inter-
fered with my devotion (such as it was) to my other
schoolwork.

Unfortunately, the marks awarded for that subject
were almost as few as the hours apportioned to it in the
school curriculum by persons of no romantic sense for
the real, ignorant of the great possibilities of active life;
with no desire for struggle, no notion of the wide spaces
of the world—mere bored professors, in fact, who were
not only middle-aged but looked to me as if they had
never been young. And their geography was very
much like themselves, a bloodless thing with a dry skin
covering a repulsive armature of uninteresting bones.

I would be ashamed of my warmth in digging up a
hatchet which has been buried now for nearly fifty
years if those fellows had not tried so often to take my
scalp at the yearly examinations. There are things
that one does not forget. And besides, the geography
which I had discovered for myself was the geography
of open spaces and wide horizons built up on men's
devoted work in the open air, the geography still
militant but already conscious of its approaching end
with the death of the last great explorer. The antagonism was radical.

Thus it happened that I got no marks at all for my
first and only paper on Arctic geography, which I
wrote at the age of thirteen. I still think that for
my tender years it was an erudite performance. I
certainly did know something of Arctic geography, but
what I was after really, I suppose, was the history of
Arctic exploration. My knowledge had considerable

gaps, but I managed to compress my enthusiasm into just two pages, which in itself was a sort of merit. Yet I got no marks. For one thing it was not a set subject. I believe the only comment made about it to my private tutor was that I seemed to have been wasting my time in reading books of travel instead of attending to my studies. I tell you, those fellows were always trying to take my scalp. On another occasion I just saved it by proficiency in map-drawing. It must have been good, I suppose; but all I remember about it is that it was done in a loving spirit.

I have no doubt that star-gazing is a fine occupation, for it leads you within the borders of the unattainable. But map gazing, to which I became addicted so early, brings the problems of the great spaces of the earth into stimulating and directing contact with sane curiosity and gives an honest precision to one's imaginative faculty. And the honest maps of the nineteenth century nourished in me a passionate interest in the truth of geographical facts and a desire for precise knowledge which was extended later to other subjects.

For a change had come over the spirit of cartographers. From the middle of the eighteenth century on the business of map-making had been growing into an honest occupation, registering the hard-won knowledge, but also in a scientific spirit recording the geographical ignorance of its time. And it was Africa, the continent out of which the Romans used to say some new thing was always coming, that got cleared of the dull imaginary wonders of the dark ages, which were replaced by exciting spaces of white paper. Regions unknown! My imagination could depict to itself there worthy, adventurous and devoted men, nibbling at the edges, attacking from north and south and east and west, conquering a bit of truth here and a bit of truth there, and sometimes swallowed up by the mystery their hearts were so persistently set on unveiling.

Among them Mungo Park, of western Sudan, and Bruce, of Abyssinia, were, I believe, the first friends I made when I began to take notice—I mean geographical notice—of the continents of the world into which I was born. The fame of these two had already been for a long time European, and their figures had become historical by then. But their story was a very novel thing to me, for the very latest geographical news that could have been whispered to me in my cradle was that of the expedition of Burton and Speke, the news of the existence of Tanganyika and of Victoria Nyanza.

I stand here confessed as a contemporary of the Great Lakes. Yes, I could have heard of their discovery in my cradle, and it was only right that, grown to a boy's estate, I should have in the later sixties done my first bit of map-drawing and paid my first homage to the prestige of their first explorers. It consisted in entering laboriously in pencil the outline of Tanganyika on my beloved old atlas, which, having been published in 1852, knew nothing, of course, of the Great Lakes. The heart of its Africa was white and big.

Surely it could have been nothing but a romantic impulse which prompted the idea of bringing it up to date with all the accuracy of which I was capable. Thus I could imagine myself stepping in the very footprints of geographical discovery. And it was not all wasted time. As a bit of prophetic practice it was not bad for me. Many years afterwards, as second officer in the Merchant Service, it was my duty to correct and bring up to date the charts of more than one ship, according to the Admiralty notices. I did this work conscientiously and with a sense of responsibility; but it was not in the nature of things that I should ever recapture the excitement of that entry of Tanganyika on the blank of my old atlas.

It must not be supposed that I gave up my interest in the polar regions. My heart and my warm participation swung from the frigid to the torrid zone, fascinated by the problems of each, no doubt, but more yet by the men who, like masters of a great art, worked each according to his temperament to complete the picture of the earth. Almost each day of my schoolboy life had its hour given up to their company. And to this day I think that it was a very good company.

Not the least interesting part in the study of geographical discovery lies in the insight it gives one into the characters of that special kind of men who devoted the best part of their lives to the exploration of land and sea. In the world of mentality and imagination which I was entering it was they and not the characters of famous fiction who were my first friends. Of some of them I had soon formed for myself an image indissolubly connected with certain parts of the world. For instance, western Sudan, of which I could draw the rivers and principal features from memory even now, means for me an episode in Mungo Park's life.

It means for me the vision of a young, emaciated, fair-haired man, clad simply in a tattered shirt and worn-out breeches, gasping painfully for breath and lying on the ground in the shade of an enormous African tree (species unknown), while from a neighbouring village of grass huts a charitable black-skinned woman is approaching him with a calabash full of pure cold water, a simple draught which, according to himself, seems to have effected a miraculous cure. The central Sudan, on the other hand, is represented to me by a very different picture, that of a self-confident and keen-eyed person in a long cloak and wearing a turban on

F

his head, riding slowly towards a gate in the mud walls of an African city, from which an excited population is streaming out to behold the wonder—Doctor Barth, the protégé of Lord Palmerston, and subsidized by the British Foreign Office, approaching Kano, which no European eye had seen till then, but where forty years later my friend Sir Hugh Clifford, the Governor of Nigeria, travelled in state in order to open a college.

I must confess that I read that bit of news and inspected the many pictures in the illustrated papers without any particular elation. Education is a great thing, but Doctor Barth gets in the way. Neither will the monuments left by all sorts of empire builders suppress for me the memory of David Livingstone. The words "Central Africa" bring before my eyes an old man with a rugged, kind face and a clipped, gray moustache, pacing wearily at the head of a few black followers along the reed-fringed lakes towards the dark native hut on the Congo headwaters in which he died, clinging in his very last hour to his heart's unappeased desire for the sources of the Nile.

That passion had changed him in his last days from a great explorer into a restless wanderer refusing to go home any more. From his exalted place among the blessed of militant geography and with his memory enshrined in Westminster Abbey, he can well afford to smile without bitterness at the fatal delusion of his exploring days, a notable European figure and the most venerated perhaps of all the objects of my early geographical enthusiasm.

Once only did that enthusiasm expose me to the derision of my schoolboy chums. One day, putting my finger on a spot in the very middle of the then white heart of Africa, I declared that some day I would go there. My chums' chaffing was perfectly justifiable.

I myself was ashamed of having been betrayed into mere vapouring. Nothing was further from my wildest hopes. Yet it is a fact that, about eighteen years afterwards, a wretched little stern-wheel steamboat I commanded lay moored to the bank of an African river.

Everything was dark under the stars. Every other white man on board was asleep. I was glad to be alone on deck, smoking the pipe of peace after an anxious day. The subdued thundering mutter of the Stanley Falls hung in the heavy night air of the last navigable reach of the Upper Congo, while no more than ten miles away, in Reshid's camp just above the Falls, the yet unbroken power of the Congo Arabs slumbered uneasily. Their day was over. Away in the middle of the stream, on a little island nestling all black in the foam of the broken water, a solitary little light glimmered feebly, and I said to myself with awe, "This is the very spot of my boyish boast."

A great melancholy descended on me. Yes, this was the very spot. But there was no shadowy friend to stand by my side in the night of the enormous wilderness, no great haunting memory, but only the unholy recollection of a prosaic newspaper "stunt" and the distasteful knowledge of the vilest scramble for loot that ever disfigured the history of human conscience and geographical exploration. What an end to the idealized realities of a boy's daydreams! I wondered what I was doing there, for indeed it was only an unforeseen episode, hard to believe in now, in my seaman's life. Still, the fact remains that I have smoked a pipe of peace at midnight in the very heart of the African continent, and felt very lonely there.

But never so at sea. There I never felt lonely, because there I never lacked company. The company of great navigators, the first grown-up friends of my early boy-

hood. The unchangeable sea preserves for one the sense
of its past, the memory of things accomplished by wisdom and daring among its restless waves. It was those
things that commanded my profoundest loyalty, and
perhaps it is by the professional favour of the great
navigators ever present to my memory that, neither
explorer nor scientific navigator, I have been permitted
to sail through the very heart of the old Pacific mystery,
a region which even in my time remained very imperfectly charted and still remote from the knowledge
of men.

It was in 1888, when in command of a ship loading in
Sydney a mixed cargo for Mauritius, that, one day, all
of a sudden, all the deep-lying historic sense of the exploring adventures in the Pacific surged up to the surface
of my being. Almost without reflection I sat down
and wrote a letter to my owners suggesting that, instead
of the usual southern route, I should take the ship
to Mauritius by way of Torres Strait. I ought to have
received a severe rap on the knuckles, if only for wasting
their time in submitting such an unheard-of proposition.

I must say I awaited the reply with some trepidation.
It came in due course, but instead of beginning with
the chiding words, "We fail to understand," etc., etc.,
it simply called my attention in the first paragraph to
the fact that "there would be an additional insurance
premium to pay for that route," and so on, and so on.
And it ended like this: "Upon the whole, however, we
have no objection to your taking the ship through
Torres Strait if you are certain that the season is not
too far advanced to endanger the success of your
passage by the calms which, as you know, prevail at
times in the Arafura Sea."

I read, and in my heart I felt compunctious. The
season was somewhat advanced. I had not been

scrupulously honest in my argumentation. Perhaps it was because I never expected it to be effective. And here it was all left to my responsibility. My letter must have struck a lucky day in Messrs. H. Simpson & Sons' offices—a romantic day. I won't pretend that I regret my lapse from strict honesty, for what would the memory of my sea life have been for me if it had not included a passage through Torres Strait, in its fullest extent, from the mouth of the great Fly River right on along the track of the early navigators.

The season being advanced, I insisted on leaving Sydney during a heavy southeast gale. Both the pilot and the tug-master were scandalized by my obstinacy, and they hastened to leave me to my own devices while still inside Sydney Heads. The fierce southeaster caught me up on its wings, and no later than the ninth day I was outside the entrance of Torres Strait, named after the undaunted and reticent Spaniard who, in the seventeenth century, first sailed that way without knowing where he was, without suspecting he had New Guinea on one side of him and the whole solid Australian continent on the other—he thought he was passing through an archipelago—the Strait whose existence for a century and a half had been doubted, argued about, squabbled over by geographers, and even denied by the disreputable but skilful navigator, Abel Tasman, who thought it was a large bay, and whose true contours were first laid down on the map by James Cook, the navigator without fear and without reproach, the greatest in achievement and character of the later seamen fathers of militant geography. If the dead haunt the scenes of their earthly exploits, then I must have been attended benevolently by those three shades—the inflexible Spaniard of such lofty spirit that in his report he disdains to say a single word about the

appalling hardships and dangers of his passage; the pig-
headed Hollander who, having made up his mind that
there was no passage there, missed the truth by only
fifty miles or so; and the great Englishman, a son of the
soil, a great commander and a great professional seaman,
who solved that question among many others and left
no unsolved problems of the Pacific behind him. Great
shades! All friends of my youth!

It was not without a certain emotion that, commanding very likely the first, and certainly the last, merchant
ship that carried a cargo that way—from Sydney to
Mauritius—I put her head at daybreak for Bligh's
Entrance, and packed on her every bit of canvas she
could carry. Windswept, sunlit empty waters were all
around me, half-veiled by a brilliant haze. The first
thing that caught my eye upon the play of green white-
capped waves was a black speck marking conveniently
the end of a low sandbank. It looked like the wreck of
some small vessel.

I altered the course slightly in order to pass close, with
the hope of being able to read the letters on her stern.
They were already faded. Her name was *Honolulu*.
The name of the port I could not make out. The story
of her life is known by now to God alone, and the winds
must have drifted long ago around her remains a quiet
grave of the very sand on which she had died. Thirty-
six hours afterwards, of which about nine were spent
at anchor, approaching the other end of the Strait, I
sighted a gaunt, gray wreck of a big American ship
lying high and dry on the southernmost of the Warrior
Reefs. She had been there for years. I had heard
of her. She was legendary. She loomed up, a sinister
and enormous *memento mori* raised by the refraction of
this serene afternoon above the far-away line of the
horizon drawn under the sinking sun.

And thus I passed out of Torres Strait before the dusk settled on its waters. Just as a clear sun sank ahead of my ship I took a bearing of a little island for a fresh departure, an insignificant crumb of dark earth, lonely, like an advanced sentinel of that mass of broken land and water, to watch the approaches from the side of the Arafura Sea. But to me it was a hallowed spot, for I knew that the *Endeavour* had been hove to off it in the year 1762 for her captain, whose name was James Cook, to go ashore for half an hour. What he could possibly want to do I cannot imagine. Perhaps only to be alone with his thoughts for a moment. The dangers and the triumphs of exploration and discovery were over for that voyage. All that remained to do was to go home, and perhaps his great and equable soul, tempered in the incessant perils of a long exploration, wanted to commune with itself at the end of its task. It may be that on this dry crumb of the earth's crust which I was setting by compass he had tasted a moment of perfect peace. I could depict to myself the famous seaman navigator, a lonely figure in a three-cornered hat and square-skirted laced coat, pacing to and fro slowly on the rocky shore, while in the ship's boat, lying off on her oars, the coxswain kept his eyes open for the slightest sign of the captain's hand.

Thus the sea has been for me a hallowed ground, thanks to those books of travel and discovery which have peopled it with unforgettable shades of the masters in the calling which, in a humble way, was to be mine, too; men great in their endeavour and in hard-won successes of militant geography; men who went forth each according to his lights and with varied motives, laudable or sinful, but each bearing in his breast a spark of the sacred fire.

THE *TORRENS:* A PERSONAL TRIBUTE

IT IS one of the pleasant surprises of my accumulated
years to be still here when the shade of that beautiful
ship is being evoked for a moment by a sea-travel
magazine before the eyes of a public which does its
sea travelling under very different conditions. Personally I cannot help thinking them not so much improved as needlessly sophisticated. However, that
opinion of mine may be wildly wrong. I am not
familiar with the demands of the spirit of the age.
And, besides, I know next to nothing of sea travel.
Even of the people who do that thing I know but few.
My two years in the *Torrens* is my only professional experience of passengers; and though we—officers brought
up in strenuous Indiamen and famous wool clippers—
did not think much of passengers, regarding them as
derogatory nuisances with delicate feelings which prevented one driving one's ship till all was blue, I will
confess that this experience was most fortunate from
every point of view, marking the end of my sea life
with pleasant memories, new impressions, and precious
friendships. The pleasant memories include the excellent ship's companies it was my luck to work with
on each of my two voyages. But the *Torrens* had
a fame which attracted the right kind of sailor, and
when engaging her crew her chief officer had always a
large and promising crowd to pick and choose from.
There was in it always a certain proportion of men who
had served in her before and were anxious to join again;
for apart from her more brilliant qualities, such as her

speed and her celebrated good looks (which by themselves go a long way with a sailor), she was regarded as a "comfortable ship" in a strictly professional sense, which means that she was known to handle easily and to be a good sea boat in heavy weather. I cannot say that during my time in her we ever experienced really heavy weather; but we had the usual assortment of winds, up to "very strong gales" (logbook style), from various directions; and I can testify that, on every point of sailing, the way that ship had of letting big seas slip under her did one's heart good to watch. It resembled so much an exhibition of intelligent grace and unerring skill that it could fascinate even the least seamanlike of our passengers. A passage under sail brings out in the course of days whatever there may be of sea love and sea sense in any individual whose soul is not indissolubly wedded to the pedestrian shore.

There are, of course, degrees of landsmanism—even to the incurable. A gentleman whom we had on board on my first voyage presented an extreme instance of it. It, however, trenched upon the morbid in its excessive sea fright, which had its pathetic as well as comic moments. We had not been more than ten days out from Plymouth when he took it into his head that his shattered constitution could not stand the voyage. Note that he had not had as much as an hour of seasickness. He maintained, however, that a few more days at sea would certainly kill him. He was absolutely certain of it, and he pleaded day after day with a persistent agonized earnestness to be put ashore on the first convenient bit of land, which in this case would have been Teneriffe. But it is not so easy for a sailing ship to make an unexpected call without losing much time. Any deviation from a direct course of the voyage (unless in case of actual distress) would have invalidated the ship's insurance. It was not to be thought of, especially as the man looked fit enough and the doctor had reported that he could not find the slightest evidence of organic disease of any sort. I was sorry for my captain. He could not refuse to listen to the man. Neither could he accede to his request. It was absurd. And yet! . . . who could tell? It became worse when he began to offer progressive bribes up to £300 or more. I don't know why I was called to one of those awful conferences. The even, low flow of argument from those trembling lips impressed me. He exhibited to us his bank passbook to prove that he had the means to buy his life from us. Our doctor stood by in grim silence. The captain looked dead-tired, but kept his temper wonderfully under the implication of callous heartlessness. It was I who could not stand the inconclusive anguish of the situation. It was not so long since I had been neurasthenic myself. At the very next pause I remarked in a loud and cheery tone, "I suppose I had better get the anchors ready first thing to-morrow." The captain glared at me speechlessly, as well he might. But the effect of the hopeful word "anchors" had an instantaneous soothing effect on our passenger. As if satisfied that there was at last somebody on his side he was willing to leave it at that. He went out.

I need not say that next day the anchors were not touched. But we sighted Teneriffe at thirty miles off, to windward—a towering and majestic shadow against the sky. Our passenger spent the day leaning over the rail, watching it till it melted away in the dusk. It was the confirmation of a death sentence for him, I suppose. He took it very well.

He gave me the opportunity to admire for many days an exhibition of consistent stoicism. He never repined

He withdrew within himself. Though civil enough when addressed directly, he had very few words to give to anybody—as though his fund of speech had been expended while pleading in vain for his life. But his heart was burning with indignant anger. He went ashore unreadable but unforgiving, without taking notice of any one in the ship. I was the only exception. Poor futile creature as I was, he remembered that I at least had seemed to be "on his side." If I may take an Irishman's privilege, I will say that if he had really died he could not have abhorred the ship and everyone in her more. To have been exposed to live for seventy days under a sentence of death was a soul-searing outrage, and he very properly resented it to the last.

I must say that, in general, our passengers would begin very soon to look thoroughly at home in the ship. Its life was homely enough and far removed from the ideals of the Ritz Hotel. The monotony of the sea is easier to bear than the boredom of the shore, if only because there is no visible remedy and no contrasts at hand to keep discontent alive. The world contains, or contained then, some people who could put up with a sense of peace for three months. The feeling of close confinement in a sailing ship, with her propelling power working in the open air, and with her daily life going on in public sight, and presenting the varied interests of human character and individual exertion, is always less oppressive than in a steamer even many times her size. Besides, in a sailing ship there are neither vibration nor mechanical noises to grow actively wearisome. Another advantage was that the sailing passenger ships of that epoch were never crowded. The cabins of the *Torrens* had two berths each, but they were roomy and not overfurnished with all sorts of inadequate contrivances for comfort, so-called. I have seen the cabins of a modern passenger steamship with three or four berths (their very couches being numbered) which were not half as big as ours. Not half as big—in fact, some of our passengers, who seized the opportunity of learning to dance the hornpipe from our boatswain (an agile professor), could pursue their studies in their own rooms. And that art requires for its practice more space than the proverbial swinging of a cat, I can assure you. Much more.

The *Torrens* was launched in 1875, only a few months after I had managed, after lots of trouble, to launch myself on the waters of the Mediterranean. Thus we began our careers about the same time. From the professional point of view hers was by far the greater success. It began early, and went on growing for fifteen years under the command of Captain H. R. Angell, whose own long career as a ship master was the greatest success of the three. He left her in 1890, and people said that he took his ship's luck away with him. The *Torrens* certainly lost some of her masts the very next voyage, by one of those sudden accidents for which no man can be made responsible. I joined her a year afterwards, on the 2d of November, 1891, in London, and I ceased to "belong to her," as the saying is (it was a wrench), on the 15th of October, 1893, when, in London Dock, I took a long look from the quay at that last of ships I ever had under my care, and, stepping round the corner of a tall warehouse, parted from her for ever, and at the same time stepped (in merciful ignorance) out of my sea life altogether.

I owed the opportunity of my close association with my famous contemporary to my acquaintance with Captain W. H. Cope, who succeeded Captain H. R. Angell. I had known him some years before, but only slightly, in a social way. I knew that he had been a

Conway boy, that he had had much varied service in
mail boats and in the Hooghly pilot steamer before the
command of the *Torrens* came in his way. But I had
no reason to believe that he remembered me particularly. However, on hearing from his brother that I
was ashore, he sent me word that the *Torrens* wanted
a chief officer, as a matter that might interest me. I
was then recovering slowly from a bad breakdown,
after a most unpleasant and persistent tropical disease
which I had caught in Africa while commanding a
steamer on the River Congo. Yet the temptation
was great. I confessed to him my doubts of my fitness
for the post, from the point of view of health. But he
said that moping ashore never did any one any good, and
was very encouraging. It was clear that, as the saying
goes, "my looks did not pity me," for he argued that,
so far as appearance went, there did not seem to be
anything the matter with me. And I suppose I could
never have been half as neurasthenic as our poor passenger who wanted to be put ashore, for I lasted out
for two voyages, as my discharges prove, though Mr.
Basil Lubbock, in his book, "The Colonial Clippers,"
credits me with only one. But in the end I had to go
(and even stay) ashore. Thus my famous contemporary outlived me at sea by many years, and if she had
perhaps a harder life of it than I, it was at least untinged
with unavailing regrets; and she escaped the ignomini-
ous fate of being laid up as a coal hulk, which so many
of her sisters had to suffer. Mr. Lubbock, who can put
so much interesting knowledge and right feeling into
his studies of our merchant ships, calls her "The Wonderful *Torrens*." She was! Her fascinations and virtues have made their marks on the hearts of men.
Only last year I received a letter from a young able
seaman, whom I remembered having in my watch,

invoking confidently her unforgotten name. "I feel sure you must be Mr. Conrad, the chief officer, in whose watch I was when serving in the *Torrens* in 1891, and so I venture to write to you. . . ." A friendly, quiet, middle-aged seaman's letter, which gave me the greatest pleasure. And I know of a retired sailor (a Britisher, I suppose), in Massachusetts, who is making a model in loving memory of her who, all her life, was so worthy of men's loyal service. I am sorry I had no time to go to see him, and to gaze at the pious work of his hands.

It is touching to read in Mr. Lubbock's book that, after her transfer to the Italian flag, when she was taken to Genoa to be broken up, the Genoese shipwrights were so moved by the beauty of her lines and the perfections of her build that they had no heart to break her up. They went to work instead to preserve her life for a few more years. A true labour of love, if ever there was one!

But in the end her body of iron and wood, so fair to look upon, had to be broken up—I hope with fitting reverence; and as I sit here, thirty years, almost to a day, since I last set eyes on her, I love to think that her perfect form found a merciful end on the shores of the sunlit sea of my boyhood's dreams, and that her fine spirit has returned to dwell in the regions of the great winds, the inspirers and the companions of her swift, renowned, sea-tossed life, which I, too, have been permitted to share for a little while.

CHRISTMAS DAY AT SEA

THEOLOGICALLY Christmas Day is the greatest occasion for rejoicing offered to sinful mankind; but this
aspect of it is so august and so great that the human
mind refuses to contemplate it steadily, perhaps because
of its own littleness, for which of course it is in no way to
blame. It prefers to concentrate its attention on cere-
monial observances, expressive generally of good will
and festivity, such, for instance, as giving presents and
eating plum-puddings. It may be said at once here
that from that conventional point of view the spirit of
Christmas Day at sea appears distinctly weak. The
opportunities, the materials too, are lacking. Of course,
the ship's company get a plum-pudding of some sort,
and when the captain appears on deck for the first
time the officer of the morning watch greets him with
a "Merry Christmas, sir," in a tone only moderately
effusive. Anything more would be, owing to the difference in station, not correct. Normally he may expect a return for this in the shape of a "The same
to you" of a nicely graduated heartiness. He does not
get it always, however.

One Christmas morning, many years ago (I was
young then and anxious to do the correct thing), my
conventional greeting was met by a grimly scathing
"Looks like it, doesn't it?" from my captain. Nothing
more. A three-days' more or less thick weather had
turned frankly into a dense fog, and I had him called
according to orders. We were in the chops of the
Channel, with the Scilly Islands on a vague bearing

within thirty miles of us, and not a breath of wind anywhere. There the ship remained wrapped up in a damp blanket and as motionless as a post stuck right in the way of the wretched steamboats groping blindly in and out of the Channel. I felt I had behaved tactlessly; yet how rude it would have been to have withheld the season's greetings from my captain!

It is very difficult to know what is the right thing to do when one is young. I suffered exceedingly from my gaucherie; but imagine my disgust when in less than half an hour we had the narrowest possible escape from a collision with a steamer which, without the slightest warning sound, appeared like a vague dark blot in the fog on our bow. She only took on the shape of a ship as she passed within twenty yards of the end of our jibboom, terrifying us with the furious screeching of her whistle. Her form melted into nothing, long before the end of the beastly noise, but I hope that her people heard the simultaneous yell of execration from thirty-six throats which we sent after her by way of a Christmas greeting. Nothing more at variance with the spirit of peace and good will could be imagined; and I must add that I never saw a whole ship's company get so much affected by one of the "close calls" of the sea. We remained jumpy all the morning and consumed our Christmas puddings at noon with restless eyes and straining ears as if under the shadow of some impending marine calamity or other.

On shore, of course, a calamity at Christmas time would hardly take any other shape than that of an avalanche—avalanche of unpaid bills. I think that it is the absence of that kind of danger which makes Christmas at sea rather agreeable on the whole. An additional charm consists in there being no worry about presents. Presents ought to be unexpected things.

The giving and receiving of presents at appointed times seems to me a hypocritical ceremony, like exchanging gifts of Dead Sea fruit in proof of sham good-fellowship. But the sea of which I write here is a live sea; the fruits one chances to gather on it may be salt as tears or bitter as death, but they never taste like ashes in the mouth.

In all my twenty years of wandering over the restless waters of the globe I can only remember one Christmas Day celebrated by a present given and received. It was, in my view, a proper live sea transaction, no offering of Dead Sea fruit; and in its unexpectedness perhaps worth recording. Let me tell you first that it happened in the year 1879, long before there was any thought of wireless messages, and when an inspired person trying to prophesy broadcasting would have been regarded as a particularly offensive nuisance and probably sent to a rest-cure home. We used to call them madhouses then, in our rude, cave-man way.

The daybreak of Christmas Day in the year 1879 was fine. The sun began to shine sometime about four o'clock over the sombre expanse of the Southern Ocean in latitude 51; and shortly afterwards a sail was sighted ahead. The wind was light, but a heavy swell was running. Presently I wished a "Merry Christmas" to my captain. He looked still sleepy, but amiable. I reported the distant sail to him and ventured the opinion that there was something wrong with her. He said, "Wrong?" in an incredulous tone. I pointed out that she had all her upper sails furled and that she was brought to the wind, which, in that region of the world, could not be accounted for on any other theory. He took the glasses from me, directed them towards her stripped masts resembling three Swedish safety matches, flying up and down and waggling to and fro ridiculously in that heaving and austere wilderness of

countless water-hills, and returned them to me without
a word. He only yawned. This marked display of
callousness gave me a shock. In those days I was
generally inexperienced and still a comparative stranger
in that particular region of the world of waters.

The captain, as is a captain's way, disappeared from
the deck; and after a time our carpenter came up the
poop ladder carrying an empty small wooden keg, of
the sort in which certain ship's provisions are packed.
I said, surprised, "What do you mean by lugging this
thing up here, Chips?"—"Captain's orders, sir," he
explained shortly.

I did not like to question him further, and so we only
exchanged Christmas greetings and he went away.
The next person to speak to me was the steward. He
came running up the companion stairs: "Have you
any old newspapers in your room, sir?"

We had left Sydney, N.S.W., eighteen days before.
There were several old Sydney *Heralds*, *Telegraphs*,
Bulletins in my cabin, besides a few home papers re-
ceived by the last mail. "Why do you ask, steward?"
I inquired naturally. "The captain would like to have
them," he said.

And even then I did not understand the inwardness
of these eccentricities. I was only lost in astonishment
at them. It was eight o'clock before we had closed
with that ship, which, under her short canvas and heading nowhere in particular, seemed to be loafing aim-
lessly on the very threshold of the gloomy home of
storms. But long before that hour I had learned from
the number of the boats she carried that this nonchalant
ship was a whaler. She was the first whaler I had ever
seen. She had hoisted the Stars and Stripes at her
peak, and her signal flags had told us already that

her name was: "*Alaska*—two years out from New York—east from Honolulu—two hundred and fifteen days on the cruising ground."

We passed, sailing slowly, within a hundred yards of her; and just as our steward started ringing the breakfast bell the captain and I held aloft, in good view of the figures watching us over her stern, the keg, properly headed up and containing, besides an enormous bundle of old newspapers, two boxes of figs in honour of the day. We flung it far out over the rail. Instantly our ship, sliding down the slope of a high swell, left it far behind in our wake. On board the *Alaska* a man in a fur cap flourished an arm; another, a much be-whiskered person, ran forward suddenly. I never saw anything so ready and so smart as the way that whaler, rolling desperately all the time, lowered one of her boats. The Southern Ocean went on tossing the two ships like a juggler his gilt balls, and the microscopic white speck of the boat seemed to come into the game instantly, as if shot out from a catapult on the enormous and lonely stage. That Yankee whaler lost not a moment in picking up her Christmas present from the English wool clipper.

Before we had increased the distance very much she dipped her ensign in thanks and asked to be reported "All well, with a catch of three fish." I suppose it paid them for two hundred and fifteen days of risk and toil, away from the sounds and sights of the inhabitated world, like outcasts devoted, beyond the confines of mankind's life, to some enchanted and lonely penance.

Christmas Days at sea are of varied character, fair to middling and down to plainly atrocious. In this statement I do not include Christmas Days on board passenger ships. A passenger is, of course, a brother (or sister), and quite a nice person in a way, but his Christmas Days are, I suppose, what he wants them to be: the conventional festivities of an expensive hotel included in the price of his ticket.

OCEAN TRAVEL

THE one statement that can safely be advanced about
travelling at sea is that it is not what it used to be. It
is different now elementally. It is not so much a matter
of changed propelling power; it is something more.
In the old days, under the machinery of sails, the
distinguished and the undistinguished travellers (of
whom there were not so very many) were wafted to
distant parts of the world by the movement of variable
air currents. Now the travelling multitudes are taken
to their destination because of the invariable resistance
of water to the screwing motion of the propeller, with
which fire (that other element) has a lot to do. The
whole affair of progress across the seas has become
much more complicated and much more precise on its
physical side. It has grown also into a marvel.

But a marvellous achievement is not necessarily
interesting. It may render life more tame than perhaps it should be. I do not mean that any marvel of
applied science can tame the wild spirit that lurks in
all men, and of which the proofs are not far to seek. It
only makes the condition of our pilgrimage less exciting.

The whole psychology of sea travel is changed.
Formerly a man setting out on a sea voyage broke away
from shore conditions and found in the ship a new kind
of home. This applied even to such comparatively
short passages as across the Atlantic. But now a man
(especially if setting out for the United States) brings
the conditions of shore life with him on board, and
finds in his ship the usual sort of hotel, with its at-

tempts at all kinds of sham comforts, all the disadvantages of gregarious life, with the added worry of not being able to get away from it for a certain number of days. The only comfort is to be found in the assurance that the number of days is not great and that, barring accidents, it is fixed. There is a definite date to look forward to—the date of release from that more or less luxurious prison any ship must be to any passenger.

That every passenger (even in the biggest and most hotel-like Atlantic ferries with their territorial names) wishes to escape there can be not the slightest doubt. He may say what he likes, but it is a fact of human nature. He looks forward to his release much as any prisoner. The modern traveller has never the time to get into an acquiescent mood. The sham shore conditions which the shipping companies try to create for him stand in the way, too. The hold of the land (which is his natural element) is on him all through the passage, and he suffers from a subtle disharmony between his natural tastes and his surroundings.

It was otherwise with the old-time traveller under sail: he had to become acclimatized to that moral atmosphere of ship life which he was fated to breathe for so many days. He was no dweller in an unpleasantly unsteady imitation of a Ritz Hotel. He would before long begin to feel himself a citizen of a small community in special conditions and with special interests which gradually ceased to be secret to him, and in the end secured his sympathies. The machinery of his propulsion, the picturesque activities of the men of the sea, lay open to his sight and appealed to his sympathies.

In the course of my sea life, a time when it never occurred to me that I myself might be a passenger some day, I was for a couple of years officer of a sailing passenger ship out of the Port of London. This gave me the opportunity to watch that process of acclimatization of which I have spoken, in a group of about sixty persons of various ages and temperaments, some travelling for their health and others only for rest—which they indubitably secured in our passages that averaged about eighty days. Part of our passengers, those from the Midlands generally, used to come on board in London Dock, while others, those from the South and from London itself preferred to join the ship in Plymouth, where we had to call in order to embark the live stock for the voyage. Of that feathered and four-footed company the most important item was the milch-cow which joined the ship mainly "for the benefit of the children," as the advertisements had it. It was the last living thing that came on board, already boxed and in its travelling stall, and displaying a most praiseworthy composure even while spinning in midair at the foreyard arm before being landed on the fore-deck against the mast, to which its straitened habitation was secured for the passage with lashings of chain and rope fit to withstand the heaviest weather we were likely to encounter.

There, on fine mornings (and there are more fine mornings at sea than have ever been dreamt of in a landsman's philosophy), the ship's children, some controlled by nursemaids, others running loose, trooped forward to pay a visit to their cow, which looked with mild big eyes at the small citizens of our sea community with the air of knowing all there was to know about them.

All this may sound very primitive, but it had a charm and an intimacy of a settled existence no modern steam-ship with its long barren alleyways swept by the wind and decorated with the name of promenade decks can give. The modern passenger may be able to walk a good many miles in his ship in the course of the day, but this is the only thing which differentiates him from the bales of goods carried in the hold—this, and the power of swallowing the food which is presented to him at regular intervals. He is carried along swiftly and fed delicately, but the other lived the life of his ship, that sort of life which is not sustained on bread (and *suprême au volaille*) alone, but depends for its interest on enlarged sympathies and awakened perceptions of nature and men.

I have seen old maiden ladies develop during a passage nice discrimination in the matter of steering. They had their favourite helmsmen. Elderly business men would become good judges of the set of the sails and acquire a seaman's eye for the aspects of the weather—and almost all, men and women, became reconciled to the vast solitude of the sea untroubled by the sound of the world's mechanical contrivances and the noise of its endless controversies. The silence of the universe would lie very close to the sailing ship, with her freight of lives from which the daily stresses and anxieties had been removed, as if the circle of the horizon had been a magic ring laid on the sea. No doubt the days thus enchanted were empty, but they were not so tedious as people may imagine. They passed quickly, and, if they brought no profit or excitement, I cannot help thinking that they were not wasted. No! They were not wasted.

OUTSIDE LITERATURE

HAVING been prompted by a certain literary suggestion to reflect upon the nature of Notices to Mariners,
I fell to examining some of my old feelings and impressions which, strictly professional as they were, have
yet contributed in the end towards the existence of a
certain amount of literature; or at any rate of pages of
prose. The Notices to Mariners are good prose but I
think no critic would admit them into the body of
literature. And it is only as compositions in prose that
I believe myself competent to speak of them. And
first let me thank God that they do not belong to
imaginative literature. It would be dreadful if they
did. An imaginatively written Notice to Mariners
would be a deadly thing. I mean it literally. It would
be sure to kill a number of people before its imaginative
quality had been appreciated and suppressed. That
their style must be clear and concise, and the punctuation of the ordinary kind, would not necessarily militate
against their being regarded as literature. The Maxims
of La Rochefoucauld are concise enough. But they
open horizons; they plumb the depths; they make us
squirm, shudder, smile in turn; and even sigh—at times;
whereas the prose of the Notices to Mariners must do
nothing of the kind.

And it doesn't. A mariner detected shuddering or
sighing over a Notice to Mariners would simply (to
speak in unliterary language) be not fit for his job.
All means of acting on man's spiritual side are forbidden

to that prose. In those compositions which are read as earnestly as anything that ever came from printing press, all suggestion of Love, of Adventure, of Romance, of Speculation, of all that decorates and ennobles life, except Responsibility, is barred. What we expect from them is not suggestion but information of an ideal accuracy, such as you do not find in the prose of the works on science, which is mainly imaginative and often solemnly mystifying. That is why some quite decent men are moved to smile as they read it. But there is no mystification in the language of truth contained in the Notices to Mariners. You would not want to smile at them. No decent man would. Even Mr. Punch, to whom as a great burlesque poet nothing is supposed to be sacred, and who has been seen lately taking liberties with the explosive atom, would not dream of making fun out of Notices to Mariners. Mr. Punch knows better. He knows that for an inspired poet who sees the mystic relations of sublunary matters, Notices to Mariners are things to be read reverently. They are like declarations of a minutely careful Providence. They can be imagined as dictated in a quiet voice by the angel who, in the words of the song, sits aloft to watch over poor Jack. They belong to a prose which, if certainly not immortal, is revelatory to its own generation.

Addressed to a special public, limited to a very definite special subject, having no connection with the intellectual culture of mankind, and yet of some importance to a civilization which is founded on the protection of life and property, that prose has only one ideal to attain, to hold on to: the ideal of perfect accuracy. You would say that such an ideal may easily be captured by a steady, prosaic mind devoting itself for a few minutes (the Notices to Mariners are short) every day to the task of composition. Why, yes! But what about misprints—the bane of authors?

And then the absences. I mean the absences of mind. It is a fact that the most pedestrian mind will sometimes take a flight from the office where it works (I suppose Notices to Mariners are written in some sort of office) toward subjects of poetic fancy, its children, its lady love, its glass of beer, and such other things interesting to its mortal envelope. I often wondered what the author of Notices to Mariners looks like. I have tried to represent him to myself as a monk, a man who has renounced the vanities of the world, and for preference belonging to the order of Trappists who are bidden to remember death—*memento mori*—and nothing else. A sobering thought! Just suppose the author of Notices to Mariners acquiring convivial habits and sitting down to write a Notice in that happy frame of mind when nothing matters much and one letter of the alphabet is as good as another. For myself—who am not convivial in that sense and have written a varied lot of prose with a quite ridiculous scrupulosity and an absurd seriousness—I don't mind confessing that if I were told to write a Notice to Mariners I would not pray perhaps—for I have my own convictions about the abuse of prayer—but I would certainly fast. I would fast in the evening and get up to write my Notice to Mariners at four o'clock in the morning for fear of accidents. One letter is so soon written for another—with fatal results.

It happened to me many years ago to endanger the course of my humble career at sea simply by writing the letter W instead of the letter E at the bottom of a page full of figures. It was an examination and I ought to have been plucked mercilessly. But in consideration, I believe, of all my other answers being correct I was handed that azimuth paper back by the examiner's assistant, with the calm remark, "You have fourteen minutes yet." I looked at the face of the clock; it was round like the moon, white as a ghost, unfeeling, idiotic. I sat down under it with the conviction of the crushing materiality of time, and calling in my mind the assistant examiner a sarcastic brute. For no man could have gone over all those figures in fourteen minutes. I hope my exasperated consternation at this check could not be detected. It was funny even to myself. Then, just at the moment when my sinking heart had touched bottom, I saw the error staring at me, enormous, gross, palpable. I traced hastily a capital E over the W and went back to the desk with my sheet of blue paper in a still shaky hand. The assistant hardly glanced at it before he let it drop, and I saw then that in my lack of comprehension it was I who had been an unqualified brute. For in his remark about the fourteen minutes he had clearly tried to give me a hint. He was a charming young man, obviously poor, with an intelligent, as if suffering, face. Not exactly sickly, but delicate. A sea voyage would have done him good. But it was I who went to sea —this time bound to Calcutta.

And it was in Calcutta, a few months afterwards, that one morning my captain on going ashore saw me busy about the decks and beckoned to me in that way ship masters have, or used to have. I mean ship masters who commanded their ships from truck to keelson as it were, technically and spiritually, in motion and at rest, and through every moment of their life, when the seaman's calling was by the mere force of its conditions more vocational than it can be at the present day. My ship master had that way of beckoning. What way? Well—all I can say of it is that one dropped everything. I can't describe it better. So I dropped whatever I was doing and he said: "You will find a Notice on the cabin table. Go in and enter it on the proper Admiralty sheet. Do it now." Which I hastened to do.

That examination, the issue of which had hung on a capital letter, had caused me to be officially certified as fit to undertake that particular duty; and ever since then my familiarity with Notices to Mariners, which are not literature, went on growing through a course of years, up to the moment when stepping ashore for the last time I lost all touch with the most trusted kind of printed prose. Henceforth I had to begin (while totally unprovided with Notices to Authors) to write prose myself; and the pains I took with it only my Maker knows! And yet I never learned to trust it. I can't trust it to this day. We who write prose which is not that of the Notices to Mariners are forgotten by Providence. No angel watches us at our toil. A dreadful doubt hangs over the whole achievement of literature; I mean that of its greatest and its humblest men. Wasn't it "Papa Augier" who, being given a copy of "Hamlet," glanced through it expertly and then dropped it with the dry remark: "*Vous appelez ça une pièce, vous?*" The whole tragedy of art lies in the nutshell of this terrifying anecdote. But it never will occur to anybody to question the prosaic force of the author of Notices to Mariners, which are not literature, and his fidelity to his honourable ideal—the ideal of perfect accuracy.

LEGENDS

To WATCH the growth of a legend is a sad occupation. It is not so much because legends deal with people and things finished and done with; that they spring, as it were, from amongst the bones of dead men. Flowers (as I have seen myself) will do that too. That's all in the order of nature, and both flowers and legends are upon the whole decorative, which is all to the good.

I have nothing against a legend twining its tendrils fancifully about the facts of history or the tables of statistics (which can be fanciful too, though they can never be made very decorative). They spring from noble soil, they are a form of memory which we all like to leave behind us, that lingers about the achievement of men who have had their day and the vanished forms of things which have served the needs of their time. One could welcome that fine form of imaginative recognition of the past with nothing worse than the gentle melancholy which the passage of time brings in its train if it were not disfigured by touches of fatuity of which no legend is wholly free, because I suspect that those who record its tales as picked out on the lips of men are doing it in a spirit of love. And that is only right and proper. But love is uncritical. It is an enthusiastic state seeing romance in what may be not true to the spirit of its subject, so to speak. And thus the false which is often fatuous also creeps into a worthy or even noble story.

Or even into a holy story. The Golden Legend itself. The legend of saints and their miracles is an awful example of that danger—as any one who turns over a few pages of it may see. Saintliness is made absurd by the presentation of the miraculous facts themselves. It lacks spirituality in a surprising way.

Yes, fatuity lurks in all legends fatally by the effect of our common credulity. However, the legend I have in my mind has nothing to do with saints—but with beings at first sight infinitely different, but whose lives were hard (no saint, I take it, ever slept on a bed of roses) if not exactly ascetic, and if not hermit-like, yet as far removed from the commonest amenities and the simplest affections which make life sweet, and as much removed from the material interests of this world as the most complete spiritual renunciation could make it.

Perhaps nobody could guess from what precedes that I have sailors in my mind. I do not mean to be irreverent if I insist that in a temporal sense there was much that was edifying in their lives. They did not work miracles, to be sure, but I have seen them repeatedly do all that men can do for their faith—if it was only the faith in their own manhood. And that is something, surely. But there was something more in it, something larger—a fidelity to the demands of their calling which I verily believe was for all of them I knew, both afloat and ashore, vocational quite as much in its way as any spiritual call a man's nature has ever responded to. And all that for no perceptible reward in the praise of man and the favour of gods—I mean the sea gods, an indigent, pitiless lot, who had nothing to offer to servants at their shrine but a ward in some hospital on shore or a sudden wedding with death in a great uproar, but with no gilding of fine words about it. *La mort sans phrases.*

In all this there is material for a fine legend, if not

of saintly virtues, then of a consistent display of
manhood. And the legend will not be long, for the
last days of sailing ships were short if one thinks of the
countless ages since the first sail of leather or rudely
woven rushes was displayed to the wind. Stretching
the period both ways to the utmost, it lasted from 1850
to 1910. Just sixty years. Two generations. The
winking of an eye. Hardly the time to drop a prophetic
tear. For the pathos of that era lies in the fact that
when the sailing ships and the art of sailing them
reached their perfection, they were already doomed. It
was a swift doom, but it is consoling to know that there
was no decadence.

That era has, however, had its historians, such as
Mr. Basil Lubbock, for instance, whose devotion to the
glory of the ships and the merits of the men has the
character of one of those romantic passions that last
a lifetime. He is now of the brotherhood initiated with
all the awful ceremonies of a Cape Horn passage. He
speaks with much knowledge. And there is Miss C.
Fox-Smith, in whom I verily believe the quintessence
of the collective soul of the latter-day seaman has found
its last resting-place and a poignant voice before taking
its flight for ever from the earth. Truth itself speaks
in her verse—I can safely say, since I (surprising
thought) have one foot, at least, in that irrecoverable
phase of old sea life for which their piety and their
talents have done so much.

It is on that ground that I would remonstrate with
Mr. Lubbock against the admission into one of his books
of sea chronicles of a tale which would degrade the
character of any legend. The facts of a legend need
not be literally true. But they ought to be credible
and they must be in a sort of fundamental accord with
the nature of the life they record, that is with the char-

acter of their subject matter. The subject of the Golden Legend is, in fact, the celebration of a miracle-working holiness, and the subject of any sea legend must be the celebration of the era of fair ships sailed with consummate seamanship—an era that seems as distant now as the age of miracles.

The history of the latter days of clipper ships and their men may be said to begin with the *Marco Polo* and the man who commanded her. His name was Forbes, and he is not a figure to stand at the head of a sea legend. He lacked balance in his character. Luck alone made him, and at the first adversity he collapsed. But without going into the details of his short career, I am sure I am doing good service to his memory by trying to purge his record of the most fatuous tale that ever cropped up in any legend of the sea.

As adopted, alas! (but the best of us may err) by Mr. Basil Lubbock, it runs that Forbes used to padlock the sheets of the *Marco Polo's* sails—one reviewer explaining kindly "to guard against the timid members of a crew," a priceless phrase, whatever it may mean. What is a "timid member" and how do you recognize him? Anyhow, I am sure he is a fitting person to play his part in that padlock story.

I wonder who was the man to tell it? He must have been an ironmonger trying for a new outlet for his wares. And to what sort of audience? Personally I would have been afraid to tell it to the Horse-Marines —that mysterious corps which is famed for its capacity to swallow anything in the way of a yarn.

[This article was left unfinished at Conrad's death.]

THE UNLIGHTED COAST

I CAME ashore bringing with me strongest of all, and most persistent, the impression of a great darkness. I do not mean darkness in a symbolic or spiritual sense. Indeed, one couldn't come from contact with the watchers of that darkness, and the workers therein, otherwise than spiritually strengthened. What I mean is the fact itself, the fact of darkness spread over the land and water of old civilization such as wrapped up early mariners' landfalls on their voyages of exploration. To him who had been accustomed to behold after long sea passages the shadowy contours of the English coast illuminated festally, interminably, unfailingly, as if for a sleepless feast or for sleepless toil, the impression was very powerful—like a revelation of some deeper truth. Fires in the night are the sign of mankind's life to an eye at sea. There were no such signs anywhere. Not a gleam. And yet life had never before perhaps in the history of that unlighted island known such an intense consciousness of itself. No! Life had not departed that sombre shore. It was only its old sense of security that was no longer there.

It had a strange air of finality. The land had turned to a shadow. Of all scourges and visitations against which mankind prays to Heaven, it was not pestilence that had smitten that shore dark; it was war; with sudden death, another of that dreaded company, full of purpose, in the air, on the water, and under the water. Breathing the calm air of the night, looking at this placid sea gleaming faintly, here and there, as still water will do in the dark, it was as hard to believe in the existence of this prowling death as in the daunt-less, tense life of that obscured land. That mere shadow—big with fate.

One seemed to have one's being in the very centre of illusory appearance. The very silence, so profound around us as to seem boundless, and harmonizing mar-vellously with the spirit of the hour, was not true to the usual meaning it conveys to a human mind, that of being cut off from communication with its kind.

For just as I was remarking to the officer by my side that surely neither Cæsar's galleys nor the ships of the Danish rovers had ever found on their approach this land so absolutely and scrupulously lightless as this—just then a voice behind us was heard: "I've here two messages I have just picked up."

It was our wireless man. That shadow emitting no sound waves, no waves of light, was talking to its watchers at sea; filling the silence with words pregnant with the truth, the naked, ugly truth of the situation.

And the man with two white pieces of paper very noticeable in his hand said: "It's our station at X speaking."

For reasons which had nothing to do with its effi-cicency we could not use our wireless installation very often, and he was immensely pleased at having picked up something for the first time in two days. We went below to de-code the messages. The little cabin, in contrast with the variously shaded and toned darkness we had left, seemed scandalously over-lighted.

Although I helped to de-code these messages I don't remember the exact words of their concise phrases; but the first was an inquiry, apparently directed at large into space, relating to a hostile submarine seen off the coast not many hours before. The other was a request addressed by name to a ship at sea for a report on some floating mines discovered in a certain position within the last twenty-four hours. The great motionless shadow was talking to its watchers, small shadows flitting here and there on the obscure gleams of the smooth sea veiled in the unmoral night that from its very nature favours aggression rather than vigilance, without regard to the merits of the case.

These were good samples of the talk that flows on unheard in sunshine, in starlight, under the clouds. War talk. But how different from the war talk we hear on the lips of men (and even great men) which often seems but talk round the war, obscuring the one and only question: To be or not to be—the great alternative of an appeal to arms. The other, the grouped-letters war talk, almost without sound and altogether without fury, is full of sense, of meaning, and single-minded purpose; inquiries, information, orders, reports. Words, too. But words in direct relation to things and facts, with the feeling at the back of it all of the correct foresight that planned and of the determination which carries on the protective work.

We all know that a true defence is at the point of the sword; but the shield has its part to play too in defensive work. This work had been planned by the navy in anticipation of the conditions that would arise. I know that praise often is but more or less conscious impertinence. But, after all, this is seamen's work, and half a lifetime at sea may perhaps justify me in expressing the highest possible sense of the navy's clear-eyed foresight in planning, and the judgment, resolution, tact, and knowledge of men in getting the planned system to work, from the first critical days to its full development of to-day, steadily, without haste, yet with that speed which is inherent in the force, unswerving purpose, and in the resolute handling of any problem under the sun.

It is mainly the officers and men of the various branches of the R.N.R. who, under the high command of naval officers, have been entrusted with the manifold duties of that simple work of protection and watchfulness. It was the navy who trained them to it, and as the period had in each case to be short, the general efficiency with which the work is done speaks well for the naval method. But it is also a high testimony to the capacity, adaptability, and the whole-souled earnestness of the officers of the Merchant Service who hastened to join, some called up, others volunteering without hesitation from all the points of the compass and from the uttermost ends of the Empire.

Much has been said already of these men and of their activities; of the circumstances, the conditions, the incidents of the task. I may perhaps later say something too, more in the nature of a personal impression than of detailed description. As to the work itself, all I want to point out now is that seen from outside it presents in its various branches the aspect of a nerve-straining drudgery. And in that outward aspect there is a proportion of truth. From its very nature it must be work without glamour. No great moments can be expected in it. Yet, rare as drops of rain in a desert, such moments have been vouchsafed to some of the faithful. As I trace these words I have in my mind the most unexpected, the most unforeseen instance of the kind. An enormous drop in a parched and stressful monotony of duty.

On the morning I heard the tale, the pier at one of our "bases," with its central line of neat shed-like buildings and the great signal bridge at the end (recalling the superstructure of a battleship), had been for a moment swept clean of all life by a rain squall as effectually as by a point-blank broadside of shrapnel shell.

My companion and I took cover in the wardroom, a good-sized apartment lined with varnished match-boarding. A heavy table occupied the middle. The officer of the watch, a silent, detached figure, sat at a writing desk reading a note, while a young bluejacket, cap in hand, waited for the answer. Two R.N.R. officers smoking by the fire greeted us. Another sat at some distance on a chair placed against the wall near a window. He took no notice of our arrival.

But the officer with me murmured with a nod in his direction: "This is our Zeppelin-strafer."

I said: "No! Have you that, too, in your lot?"

"Yes. He'll tell you all about it."

I was introduced with a word or two of comment to "our Zeppelin-strafer." There was no halo around his head. He was young, so young that he must have belonged to the third generation of those who had gone to sea since my time; one of those who began that life after 1900. A seaman of the twentieth century! And yet he was no stranger to me. The memories of my twenty sea years crowded upon me, memories of faces, of temperaments, of expressions. And looking at him, all I could say to myself was:—How like! We sat down side by side near the window. He was in no haste to begin. He belonged to the shy, silent type —and how like!

It's an odious thing to have to write in "descriptive" fashion of men with whom one talked like a friend and had found acceptance as one of themselves. If he sees these lines I hope he will forgive me. It's very likely that my impressions set down truthfully are altogether untrue. We were but half an hour together and when we parted and he closed the door of that room behind him I felt that he was as utterly gone from me as though he had stepped out in the middle of the Pacific.

He began to talk to me with a sort of reluctance, hesitatingly, till I mentioned to him that I had been to sea much longer than himself, if not so recently. He knew I was some sort of writing man, and was ready to be civil, but after that remark of mine his articulation became easier. Not much, though. He looked down on the ground, glancing at me only now and again, and spoke in a low tone with unexpected pauses. The best way in which I can characterize that narrative is by saying that he delivered it to me with the aspect, the bearing of a man who broods over the event in silence.

He was making his way on a foggy day back to his base after a spell of duty outside. His craft mounted one gun; and without going into unnecessary description I may best give an idea of the size of his command by saying that, when he was reposing, the breech of the gun was within four feet of his head as it lay on his pillow. For reasons that need not be stated, his vessel did not move then more than about three knots through the water—which was smooth. There's seldom much wind with thick weather. On that occasion there was a very light breeze, enough to help the fog at its usual pranks of thinning and thickening, opening and shutting, lifting in patches and closing down suddenly—quicker than a wink, sometimes.

He was walking up and down his vast deck when, turning aft, he saw the fore-end of a Zeppelin emerge into misty view out of an apparently thicker layer of fog. From then on for succeeding minutes he moved no more than a ship's timber. The apparition took him completely unawares because he had not heard any noise in the air before. Directly, however, he caught sight of the Zeppelin he heard the noise of the engine very plainly.

As soon as he regained the power of speech he uttered the words "Action . . . Zeppelin . . . Astern," in a cautious whisper. An unnecessary precaution. But he told me that at first the "enormous thing seemed right on top of us!" In fact, it was not anything so near as that. It was coming up astern but a little on one side and, he noticed, steering a course which would cross obliquely his wake and bring the monster very close indeed—within 500 yards perhaps.

For whatever reason, it was flying low, so low that he did not need to throw his head up much to watch its steady progress. And there followed for him such moments of unforgettable anguish, something like the anguish of a man whose eternal salvation would depend on the soundness of his judgment.

The problem was how to deal with this gigantic piece of luck. For if he opened fire too soon the chances were that the German would swerve and get away, or, climbing overhead, would descend on him as low as he pleased and bomb him out of existence. His gun was a very good weapon of its kind, but it was not an anti-aircraft gun and had only a limited amount of elevation. And there was also the possibility that, utterly unconscious of the tiny speck lost in the shimmer of the thin fog layer below, the Zeppelin would alter its course at any moment for some purpose of its own.

What worried and discomposed him was the insistent whispering of his skipper, who had crept to his elbow and was entreating hoarsely not to waste a moment, "to let the beggar have it now, sir. Let him have it." The German meantime held on. Ordering the skipper away he had the fortitude, though his heart was in his mouth all the time, to hold out till the Zeppelin crossed his wake and exposed the greater part of its side. . . . "And then," he said, "we started to plug it into him as fast as we could load. And every shot was a hit."

He looked at me with strangely troubled eyes. "It was impossible to miss . . . you know," he added in a lowered voice.

Whether conscious or unconscious before of the microscopic strafer below, Fritz must have had the surprise of his life. The record shock of Zeppelin history. His dismay was boundless, something very like panic up there became visible to the eyes below.

. . . "I could see three or four of them running along," went on the low voice. "I saw them quite plainly. If I had had half-a-dozen men with rifles on my deck we could have got every single one of them."

The Zeppelin swung off wide and with its engines working noisily, made off without more ado. Its own speed or the drift of denser fog blowing over turned it into a mere dark blur swiftly. As long as the faintest shadow of it remained visible the fire was kept up. Then it ceased. A profound silence ensued. It was all over. He was gone.

It was, however, possible that he might return overhead and take his revenge. But before the strafers on deck had the time to exchange glances of wonder, apprehension, or inquiry, while they were still, in fact, staring into the upper fog, the shadow reappeared nearer than before aslant in the white space, sliding downwards stern first, its nose tilted up at a perilous angle.

"Of course we opened on him instantly," he went on. "And do you know what he did then?"

At this point he looked at me again, and after a little

*G

gasp went on, as if unwillingly, "he dumped all his bombs overboard. The whole lot of them at once."

The resulting explosion was something terrific. He felt as if his little craft were blown clean out of the water and at the same time hit by a tidal wave. And in the awful commotion, uproar, and black smoke the Zeppelin shot up and vanished for good.

"You must have made him very sick," I said.

"He looked very sick indeed," said the young strafer quietly.

"I wonder what became of him?"

"Hard to say. There was a report in the papers some time afterwards. . . . Damaged Zeppelin coming to the ground in Norway. . . . I sometimes think . . ."

He did not finish the sentence. He had been eighteen months of long days and longer nights at his protecting work, out and in, fair or foul, never seeing anything to reward his strained, hopeful vigilance, and sometimes for days seeing nothing at all. For the North Sea is a big place, as our coasters say: so big that there may be half-a-dozen ships out looking for you because you are a little late in returning (as it happened to a man), and you will come in innocently, having seen no one, unseen by anybody—which is vexing for the anxious searchers.

Eighteen patient, unfaltering months, and then this ten gloriously crowded minutes—is that much? The whole affair probably did not last so long.

Rare, like drops of water in a desert, are such opportunities for the watchers of the lightless shore. And to this one Fortune had not been fickle, but simply outrageous. The drop had merely brushed past his lips so unskilled in speech. He had talked to me in all friendliness, for which I am duly grateful; yet he left me with the impression that had he been permitted to taste the full flavour, his official report would have remained, of his own choice, his first and last utterance. I fancy, somehow, that rather than talk of luck so immense that there could be no fit words for it in the world, he would have preferred to brood over it in adequate silence.

THE DOVER PATROL

THE worth of a sentiment lies in the sacrifices men will make for its sake. All ideals are built on the ground of solid achievement, which in a given profession creates in the course of time a certain tradition, or, in other words, a standard of conduct. The existence of a standard of conduct in its turn makes the most improbable achievement possible, by augmenting the power of endurance and of self-sacrifice amongst men who look to the past for their lessons and for their inspiration.

The story of the achievement of the Dover Patrol is merged in the greater proud record of the navy's protective part played with simplicity and self-sacrifice in the Great War of the twentieth century; yet that story has its own features, its own particular atmosphere, and its own importance.

The opening years of the nineteenth century had their Great War, too. Longer in its duration, it was carried on with less animosity. It was less in the nature of a struggle for dear life, and, except in its spirit, it was less intensely national. It did not involve in its toils the whole population. The issues at stake were as great, perhaps, but did not appear in such definite shapes to the great mass of the people which suffered its hardships and gave up its sons to its struggles. In its most obvious aspect that war, like the one of our day, was waged against an attempt at universal dominion. But it must be admitted that it was also a war against the revolt of new-born ideas represented by a great and dominant figure issued from a revolution and taking its own fatally conquering way amongst the imperfectly awakened nations of Europe. It was a struggle of the old certitudes against a man embodying the new force of subversive beliefs. It ran its course, as momentous, if less ruthless, than the deadly struggle in which the Dover Patrol has played its part. When it ended it left the world as weary, indeed, as it is to-day, but much less unsettled in its thoughts and emotions about the spiritual value of its monstrous experience. Men's ideas were simpler then, their sentiments less complex. Their desires and hopes, as poignant perhaps, remained still obscure. The instinctive reaction against all the cruel negations a war imposes on humanity had a less resentful character; and men's judgment of the attained issue was less embittered by the effort they had been called upon to make. Yet their personal feelings were much like our own.

When the hour of peace struck in 1815 there must have been on board the King's ships anchored in the Downs, patrolling in the Channel, in the squadrons on distant stations, and in others cruising off nearly every port of northern Europe—there must have been the feeling that there never would be such a war again; a feeling of relief, mingled, no doubt, with a half-acknowledged sense of regret for the occupation that was gone. The great question arising at the end of every prolonged effort made by mankind—And now—what next? asked without misgivings in the consciousness of an accomplished duty—was not free from a certain uneasiness as to the days that would follow in other and unknown conditions. For a whole generation had grown from boyhood to maturity with no knowledge of peace conditions, and unperturbed by moral doubts of its warlike achievement.

Amongst the men of the Dover Patrol assembled to see the unveiling of the memorial to their own unforgettable dead there will be also a feeling of regret for those days that are past, regret of the strenuous life with its earnest purpose, its continuity of risk, its sense of professional efficiency, its community of desperate toil; regret even of those moments of extreme bodily fatigue associated with that feeling of spiritual exaltation which enabled them each in his station, from the Admiral commanding to the youngest member of a small drifter's crew, to defy the enmity of nature and the hostility of men.

Nobody would dream of apportioning shares of importance in the great task of the navy, so varied in its unity, so diverse in its singleness of aim and its invariable purpose. But it is a fact that amongst all those activities directed to the same end, exposed to the same risk, making the same appeal, and entered upon with the same courage, the work of the Dover Patrol was very special work. The Dover Patrol held the southern exit of the North Sea in the same way in which the Grand Fleet may be said to have held its northern entrance; and the greatness of its responsibility may be appreciated from the one dominant fact: that on that Patrol rested the safety of our communications with the army in France, and that one of its achievements was the safe passage across the Channel of about seven million men without a single instance of failure, in the presence of a superior enemy established in force within easy striking distance on the flank of the line; an enemy superior in numbers and material, holding in his hands every element of successful attack except for just a portion, an ever so small portion, of that sea spirit animating the officers and men of the Dover command who stood in his way—including the very workers on shore in repair workshops and fitting-out sheds.

There was never a greater accord of fearless executive energy and skilled hard work than in the Dover Patrol. From the point of view of its spiritual harmony it was worthy to hold the extreme right wing of the great sea defence. Of its material success we all know by now; we have all heard of the millions of men transported to and fro across the Straits, of miles of nets laid along the coasts and kept in repair in defiance of heavy seas and long-range batteries, of mines swept along routes equalling in length twelve times the circumference of the globe, of merchant fleets of a hundred ships and more shepherded every day through the Downs. The eloquence of arithmetical figures as applied to the merits of the Dover Patrol is overwhelming indeed; but no figure of rhetoric can render justice to the quiet resolution of the men making up for the inadequacy of the means, the unavoidable inadequacy of the means for which only the force of circumstances was responsible, for which no past government can be blamed, since no one could have guessed the enormous scale of material requirements.

The means were inadequate, woefully inadequate; and thus the only trumps the Admiral of the Dover Patrol held in his hand at every turn of the dreadful game were the physical endurance, the inborn seamanship, the matter-of-fact, industrious, indefatigable enthusiasm with which every one under his orders threw his very soul into his appointed task. Threw it in and kept it there. It was no momentary effort. For the anxious days of the Dover Patrol were to be many, its nights full of dangers, its problems exacting, its duty calls incessant, and its men after all but the flesh and blood of our common humanity. Their souls were the only trumps in the desperate game, as he who was in command must have felt at every moment of night and day. It was a great and successful game, but it must be confessed that for more than half the time it was a game of bluff. It came off at every deal, England's usual luck, that this time, too, has not failed her at the hour of need! And England may well be proud of her traditional luck in the character of her children serving her at sea, on shore, and in the air.

The activities of the Dover Patrol were of many kinds, but there were three imperative duties to which all its energies had to be devoted: the safety of the troop-transport service, the protection of merchant shipping, the closing of the Channel exit against the German submarines. One need not insist on their vital importance for the army and the nation or on the deadly danger of even a temporary failure. The work had to be carried out with the slenderest conceivable means, with obsolete torpedo destroyers, and with unarmed drifters, in the presence of an enemy of superior force and possessing an infinite advantage in his power to choose his own time for an attack of the most deadly kind. Those three purely naval problems required incessant hard work, incessant risk, and incessant vigilance. The routine of the Dover Patrol included the boarding of ships, the regulation of traffic along the cleared war lane, the laying of net and mine barrages on the Belgian coast and across the Channel, their guard and maintenance in all weathers and in all circumstances, with always present in all minds the sense of numerical inferiority in a mission the failure of which might have well brought about something not very far from national disaster. In such conditions the stress put upon the fortitude of every individual was bound to be very great.

The Dover Patrol was equal to it. Its devotion, expressed in a plodding, dogged perseverance, stood the test of frequent severe losses in men and ships, and of continuous severe strain on its mental and physical faculties as a whole. The tale of the Dover Patrol is the tale of a small nucleus of ships and crews of the Royal Navy, and round it of a great number of other men and other vessels, mostly fisher-folk and fisher-craft, with the addition of Merchant Service men and of R.N.R. and R.N.V.R. officers and ratings. Though, properly speaking, not belonging to the fighting service, all those men lived up to their old tradition and were found sufficient for the trust reposed in them.

They were found sufficient. No praise could be more adequately expressed, when one looks at the magnitude of the trust and the arduous character of the operations it imposed upon the men and the ships of the Dover command. Originating in the simple Downs Boarding Flotilla, under the orders of the naval officer commanding at Harwich, the Dover Patrol developed an independent existence and by the establishment of fortified German naval bases on the coast of Flanders acquired an importance in the scheme of naval defence which cannot well be exaggerated. The reinforcements and supplies for the army, the food for the country, demanded the safety of the Straits. Had the enemy probed the weakness of the Dover Patrol and broken with his overwhelming force through that thin defence to invade the waters of the Channel, it would have been a disaster, the fatal consequences of which imagination even now shrinks from contemplating.

The great sailor-like qualities of the Dover Patrol,

the consummate seamanship displayed in the planning and execution of its incessant operations, its steady manner of meeting deadly emergencies, its cool vigilance in the presence of an ever-menacing situation, may well compel the admiration of any man who knows something, however little, of the demands of sea service. To the risks of actual warfare the crews of the drifters watching over the barrage nets were often helplessly exposed. But nothing could dismay either the naval or the auxiliary branches of the Dover Patrol. These men were concerned about the perfection of their work, but the sudden flash of German guns in the night troubled them not at all. As, indeed, why should it? In their early days some of them had but a single rifle on board to meet the three four-inch guns of German destroyers. Unable to put up a fight and without speed to get away, they made a sacrifice of their lives every time they went out for a turn of duty; they concentrated their valour on the calm, seamanlike execution of their work amongst the exploding mines and bursting shells. It was their conception of their honour, and they carried it out of this war unblemished by a single display of weakness, by the slightest moment of hesitation in the long tale of dangerous service.

In this simple way these seamen, professional and unprofessional, naval and civilian, have earned for themselves the memorial erected to their faithful labours. The record of the Dover Patrol's work contains a great moral and a good many professional lessons for their children and their successors; the incalculable value of a steady front, the perfecting of nets, the exact process of laying barrages in a tideway, the evolving of an ingenious method for night bombardments, and of a system of long-range firing—a whole great store of new ideas and new practice laid up for future use. But in truth that which in the last instance kept the German forces from breaking disastrously on any dark night into the Channel, and jeopardizing the very foundations of our resisting power, was not the wonderfully planned and executed defences of nets and mines, but the indomitable hearts of the men of the Dover Patrol.

MEMORANDUM

On the Scheme for Fitting Out a Sailing Ship for the Purpose of Perfecting the Training of Merchant Service Officers Belonging to the Port of Liverpool

ASSUMING that the generous public spirit of the Liverpool shipowners will find the capital necessary for the building and equipping a southern-going sailing ship to perfect the training of the officers of the Mercantile Marine, I conceive that the cost of running such a ship—that is: wages, upkeep, repairs, general surveys and insurance—ought to be covered by what she may earn as a cargo carrier on the training voyages which will be planned for her.

Here I will submit to the originators of the scheme that a voyage to an Australian port (including New Zealand) out by the Cape and round by the Horn would be the best for such a purpose. My reasons are: the healthy climate of that part of the world, the number of the meteorological regions traversed which will develop sound judgment as to weather, the comparative facility of the voyage, combined with a great variety of general experience which a round trip of that sort will offer. The length of passages need not be an objection; the complete training of a young seaman ought to include the experience of many days together at sea between water and sky. It would have a spiritual and practical value for him even if he is destined never to

be out of sight of land for more than a few days in his
future professional life.

I

Assuming then that the ship would be expected to
be self-supporting (and no more) it is my deliberate
opinion that her size should be limited strictly to the
tonnage which will enable her under modern conditions
to pay her expenses. I venture to suggest (however
shocking it may appear to the minds of men who own
and manage fleets of large steamships) fourteen to
fifteen hundred tons, or as near thereto as is consistent
with the earning of her expenses, as the proper tonnage
for the ship. I admit that I don't know what the best
freight-carrying capacity of a ship is at the present
time; but I beg the Committee charged with the elabo-
ration of the scheme to allow me to expose my reasons
for what I advance in support of the above opinion.
I must premise here that in all that I am going to say
I will be drawing on my own experience as a seaman
trained to his duties under the British flag and, in
regard to the performance of such duties, having a good
record for more than sixteen years of sea life, both in
sail and steam.

My contention is that for sea-going qualities, ease
of handling, quickness in manœuvring, and even in
point of actual safety, if caught in a bad position,
nothing can beat a, say, 1400-ton ship, designed so as
to have a dead weight carrying capacity of about once
and a half her registered tonnage. The same remark
may be applied to the comfort in bad weather when,
it must be remembered, the men managing her propelling machinery must remain exposed on the deck
instead of being sheltered under it. The latest big
sailing ship (in so far as she still exists) is generally in

that respect what the sailors graphically describe as a mere "bathing-machine," her enormous main deck, especially when running before a heavy sea, being always full of water and extremely uncomfortable, besides being dangerous for that very reason. Also, the great length necessarily given to those big ships of three thousand tons and over makes them clumsy to handle, anything but quick in manœuvre, and renders them rather helpless, from their very size, in case of any serious damage either aloft or about the rudder. It is also to be remarked that a ship's quick response in manœuvring develops a corresponding activity and smartness in her crew.

I beg the gentlemen concerned with this scheme to understand that I am not speaking as a literary person indulging his fancy but as the usual sort of Merchant Service officer who has served in all sorts of ships and draws upon his ordinary experience; with this advantage, only, that he had time to think about it and meditate over its lessons. Pursuing the matter further, I wish also to touch on the question of the ship's appearance. In a steamship the increase of size certainly makes for good looks, adding to the inherent beauty of the lines an expression of power and dignity which arouses one's admiration. It is not so with a sailing vessel. Hardly any ship of over 2000 tons I have ever seen escaped giving an impression which may be best defined by the word "overgrown"; and I have a good many in my memory to whom nothing but the sailors' graphic phrase "a big, clumsy brute" could in justice be applied. Now, in view of the end which the Liverpool shipowners have in equipping a sailing ship, that is to *perfect* the training of officers for their fleets, certain ideal elements must be taken into consideration. It is very necessary that those

boys should grow attached to their ship (an easy thing
for a sailor to do), be proud of her individual appearance, of her sea qualities, of their association with her;
and that they should remember their period of training,
not as a horrible grind in discomfort and without personal gratification of any kind, but as a great time in
their lives; an experience it has been their privilege
as seamen of the Port of Liverpool to go through; a
time to be remembered with pleasure and pride, somewhat as an old public-school boy looks back at his old
school, the beauty of its old buildings and the prestige
of its traditions. The greatest achievements of Merchant Service seamen have been performed in ships of
between 900 to 1600 tons, in the way of record passages
(which were then the exclusive merit of seamen), of
feats in clever handling and in the bringing in of disabled ships to port by their own seamanship and determination without any outside assistance. And if
the objection is made that I am advocating things hope-
lessly out of date, then my answer will be that in this
scheme of *perfected* training associated so closely with
men's *morale* and with old traditions, the out-of-
dateness argument does not apply. On the practical
side that objection may be met by pointing out that
those boys are not to be trained for officers of modern
sailing ships, but to be *perfected* as future officers of the
finest modern steamships. Therefore, what is important is to give them for their training not the most
modern sailing ship (which in any case is doomed and
need not be taken into consideration at all), but to se-
lect for them the *best* period of sailing-ship practice
and service.

One more consideration I want to present to the
originators of the scheme, which is this: that in a very
large sailing ship there is always a tendency to sup-

ply her (on account of the difficulty of manning her
effectively) with a lot of labour-saving appliances.
This brings me to the second postulate which, after the
size of the ship, I am most anxious to submit for consideration. And it is this:

II

That there should be no labour-saving appliances in
the shape of steam winches and so on; and that the
hoisting of the sails, the working of the boats, and the
general physical work of the sailor's calling should be
done by man power, of which, of course, the cadets
on board would be the principal part. A vertical
boiler, mainly for the purpose of heaving up the anchors,
may be advisable; but the windlass should be of the
kind which can be also worked by the crew by means
of a capstan on the forecastle-head.

My reasons for this insistence on the use of man
power are as follows: First of all, there is no necessity
for anything else. With forty boys out of any given
batch on board (Mr. Holt mentions eighty as the
number and on that point I will offer a remark later)
of an advanced physical development and certain weight
of body, together with a ship's crew of, say, twelve
A. B.'s, four petty officers, and some other ratings, the
officers ought to be able to handle a ship, of the size
and rig I am thinking of, like a plaything. Secondly,
it may be laid down as an axiom that no labour done on
board ship in the way of duty is either too hard or in any
way unworthy of the best effort and attention or, so
to speak, beneath the dignity of any youngster wishing
to fit himself to be a good officer. Thirdly, there is
undoubtedly something elevating in physical work into
which one puts all one's heart in association with
others and for a clearly understood purpose. Apart

from that it will bring these youths into a more intimate contact with the propelling machinery of the ship and they will, so to speak, learn the feel of it. It mustn't be forgotten that seamen's work was never looked upon or had the character of mere slavish toil, as some branches of labour on shore tend to become. In its essence life at sea has been always a healthy life, and part of that was owing to the very nature of the physical exertions required. I affirm with profound conviction that sailing-ship life is an excellent physical developer. I have repeatedly seen a delicate youngster brought on board by an anxious relative change out of all knowledge into a stout youth during a twelve-month's voyage. I have never seen an apparently delicate boy break down under the conditions of the sea life of my time. They *all* improved. Moreover, any physical work intelligently done develops a special mentality; in this case it would be the sailor mentality; surely a valuable acquisition for a sea officer either in sail or steam.

III

The sailing ship, then, I have in my eye (something very much like the Liverpool *Sierras* which were afloat between '80 and '90) would be a hull of between 1400 and 1500 tons register with a dead weight capacity of over 2000 tons, in which case it would be sufficient for her to have three square-rigged masts. If the tonnage of the ship is raised to 2000 tons register then there must be four masts, of which the aftermost one would be rigged fore and aft. In any case, I would advocate for the training ship a long poop and a very roomy forecastle head; the poop, if the vessel is three-masted, extending as far as the main rigging; and the object being to reduce the area of the main deck as much as possible. This would tend to make the ship much more comfortable. Ships with long poops are always the driest in all weathers and safest for the individuals having to move about the decks in heavy weather. The main deck would have on it a deck house in the space between the fore coaming of the main hatch and the foremast; leaving a clear passage across at each end and having wide alleyways on each side. The house would contain the vertical boiler for raising steam for the windlass; the accommodation for the ship's crew and the berths of the ship's petty officers. Under the forecastle head there would be space at the sides for various storerooms, or the electric light plant, if carried, could be installed on one side and the store-rooms on the other. All that, however, may be left to the skill and ingenuity of the designer, once the actual size of the ship and the number of people she has to carry, all told, has been decided upon.

In this matter I have a certain competence because I was for 2 years chief officer of a sailing passenger ship running between London and Adelaide and I believe the very last of her kind, with the exception perhaps of the *Macquarrie* (later training ship for New Zealand merchant cadets), where the experience of a compara-tively large number of persons on board ship could be obtained by the sailing-ship officer. She was only 1270 tons register and the greatest number of people I had on board of her was 113 all told. She had room for 50 passengers when full and we had perforce to carry a lot of live stock, a milk cow for the children and so on; yet her space was not inconveniently crowded, and no passenger ever complained of cramped accom-modation, and generally they made the round trip in her. She carried outwards a general cargo and in Adelaide loaded the usual Australian cargo, for the

most part wool. Her poop was 78 feet long over all;
under that we carried eleven double passenger cabins
on each side, two cabins for the mates, a large pantry
amidships and a doctor's berth and surgery. The accommodation for the captain consisted of two stern
cabins, both very roomy, of which one was his stateroom and the other was planned and furnished as a
sitting room, which he never used at sea, sharing the
saloon with the passengers. This saloon contained two
long tables at which all the people berthed under the
poop deck could sit down to meals. I think that this
arrangement could be adopted with advantage in the
cadet ship under contemplation. The artificial lighting
of the *Torrens* being oil and candles required extreme
vigilance, but assuming the Liverpool cadets berthed
in cabins as above, if electric light is to be introduced the lamps could be set in the partitions between them, so that each lamp would light two cabins.
The long saloon would be the common room for navigational studies and meals, the electric lighting of that
space, however economically applied, would be always
better than the lamp-lighting of that ship which was
sufficient for the passengers to read, write, or play their
games in the evening. There were never any complaints
on that score. The captain of a training ship would
probably use all his accommodation at sea too, messing
by himself. Apart from that it seems to me that the
man entrusted with the responsible position of commanding such a training ship would wish to keep in as
close touch with the boys as conformable with the preservation of proper merchant-ship discipline; and that
he would not find the nearness of his cabin to the bulk
of them either inconvenient or irksome.

The accommodation on the poop, being sufficient
only for about 44 cadets, could be duplicated to a cer-

tain extent below, aft, on the twin deck, and be made
accessible by means of the after hatch, fitted with a
proper companionway. There may be some difficulty
with the supply of daylight down there and in that
respect the berths below would be inferior, but as there
would be no doubt different grades among the boys in
the way of seniority and ratings, a boy would be
moved by seniority or on promotion from below to
above at some time or other in the course of his training. This would be something to look forward to;
and in this connection I would remark that the comfort
of the boys should be cared for strictly within the
limits of due regard for their health, physical development and opportunity for study, and no more. The
greatest simplicity in such arrangements compatible
with health and self-respect should be the note; and
I believe that no boy properly constituted and wishing
to be a seaman will resent such a system.

I suppose that as regards the boys, at least, a three-
watch system will be introduced; though I must confess
that I have never seen a boy hurt by the watch and
watch duty which in my time all of them had to go
through during the four years of their apprenticeship.
In that case, however, the utmost vigilance and alertness in the time of duty should be exacted by the
officer of the watch from the cadets at their various
stations, whether at the lee helm with the helmsman, or
on the lookout with an A. B. of the ship's crew, or about
the decks at the different sheets, tacks and braces they
may be specially told off to. The disadvantage of the
three-watch system is that the cadet will be always on
duty at the same hours. Some system of shifts should
be introduced if only to change the boys in rotation
from one watch to another; for the habit of wakefulness
is also a matter of training, and the boys should be

accustomed to keep their alertness at all periods of the night. I would suggest that the senior cadets (especially those who had obtained the rating of cadet petty officer) should be employed as assistants to the officer of the watch to the fullest possible extent; and when sufficiently advanced be entrusted with the trimming of the yards, the taking in or setting of light sails in manageable weather, and so on. The progression of stations will be, I imagine, from waist-cadets to mizzen-topmen, through main and fore to forecastlemen, which last would be selected from the strongest and the most advanced, during the training course of eighteen months. I imagine that the training ship with some luck in her weather and with quick dispatch at either end, could do two round voyages in that time. The *Torrens*, a fast ship, could have done it with ease, though as a matter of fact she made one voyage every eleven months, but then she would lie for weeks on the berth, both in London and Port Adelaide.

That ship carried four anchors, that is, three bowers and one stream, besides one big and one small kedge, and this is the number that would be sufficient for the training ship. Of course, the anchors would be stock anchors. In this connection I wish to remark that if the anchor is hove up by steam the catting and fishing should be done by hand under all circumstances with the help of the forecastle-head capstan. As to the sails, I assume that she would carry (unless she is to be really a very big ship) six topsails, three topgallantsails, three royals, four or three headsails, the usual number of staysails; and, I suggest, two courses. The crossjack course may be done away with. In my first year on board the *Torrens* we abolished that sail mainly out of regard for the feelings of the passengers who had their chairs placed all about the mizzenmast; and it made no

difference whatever to the speed of the ship. The fair
weather mizzen staysail, which was a particularly big
sail, replaced it perfectly at all trims, from sharp up
to two points abaft the beam. With the wind aft the
crossjack was merely a nuisance.

I advocate the ship carrying single topgallantsails
as a matter of traditional practice and training. For
the same reason I would suggest that the clew lines of
the upper sails and the clew-garnets of the courses
should be led to the quarters of the yard and not to the
yardarm. The proper furling of a sail, with a smooth
bunt and tightly rolled yardarms, was a great point in
the habits of smartness and proper merchant-ship discipline. It was also a matter of correct seamanship,
because a sail that was not properly furled in bad
weather was likely to free itself and blow away from
the yard. The shifting of clew lines to the yardarms was
really a dodge of undermanning, since it is obvious that
with no bunt to the sail less men are required to make
some sort of furl of it. The training ship, however, will
be anything but undermanned, and unless she were very
big there would be plenty of hands in her to furl the
three topgallantsails together. I have repeatedly seen
the four boys of the *Torrens* with the addition of one
able seaman furl the main topgallantsail of that ship
in a stiff breeze. In a ship of 1600 tons six boys and
two able seamen ought to master a topgallantsail in
almost any weather. When I joined the *Torrens* the
then master of her, Captain Cope (an old Conway boy),
fell in at once with my suggestion to shift the clew lines
back to the quarters of the yard, on the ground that the
ship was manned well enough to do things properly.

In regard to boats, I will again refer to my experience
of the *Torrens* (a sailing ship with a hundred souls on
board). We carried in her, aft, two quarter-boats on

davits abreast the mizzen rigging. They were well above water, toggled-in against a spar so as to be disengaged by one single jerk on a lanyard (their tackle falls being always coiled clear on deck), and in other respects were ready for lowering instantly. Owing to the shortness of a merchantman's crew the orders as to these boats were that in an emergency the nearest men (up to four) were to get into her at once, the officer of the watch and the midshipman of the watch attending to the falls. The only real test of quickness we had happened in the daytime and in light weather, when the ship was luffed up till the sails lifted and one of the quarter-boats was lowered to pick up a parrot which had flown overboard. Not having been on deck at the time I don't know how long all this took, but the parrot survived the experience; so we must have been quick enough to have saved a child, for instance, of which we always had several on board.

On the skids abaft the mainmast we carried two bigger spare boats bottom up and not ready for lowering. But the principal boats of the ship were two very roomy lifeboats, carried on skids forward, just abaft the fore rigging. They stood in chocks and their davits were fore-and-afted at sea, but the lowering tackles were always hooked and the falls coiled in tubs secured on the top of the deck house, of which I have spoken before. Those lifeboats were fitted out ready to "abandon ship," with sea anchors, oil bags, oars, mast and sail, blue lights, water beakers and ship's bread in tins. Their chocks were held in position by a bolt in the usual way and the ship's carpenter was instructed when making his report to me in the morning to report: "Davits and bolts free." When the bolt was knocked out a lift of three inches was all that was necessary to swing out those lifeboats. Now and again

I had a test, generally at eight o'clock in the morning
at the change of watches, and I managed to bring things
to a point when the whole operation took seven minutes
from the time of the order: "Both watches. Out
lifeboats," to the moment when they were swung back
and landed again in their chocks; the second mate taking charge of the starboard and the senior apprentice
(acting third) of the port side. This for a merchant
ship was quite as good as could be expected and would
have met almost any emergency short of sudden disaster. In the Channel and between the chops of the
Channel and the Western Islands (either homeward or
outward bound), on the first appearance of thick
weather with a moderate sea, it was a standing order
that the officer of the watch immediately after calling
the captain was to swing these boats outboard ready
for lowering. In that position they remained, weather
permitting, till the fog cleared.

I have entered into those details because from the
nature of things there can be very few sailing-ship
officers left now who have had the experience of the
care of upwards of a hundred people on board a 1300-
ton ship. How far the boys should be given an insight
into the stowage of a large single hold I am not prepared
to say. The proper stowage of a sailing ship was an
extremely important part of her preparation for sea,
affecting her sailing powers, the comfort of everybody
on board, and even her absolute safety. The stowage
of a subdivided hold of a large steamship is from the
very nature of things a much less nice matter. It is
also different in its nature, since the order of the ports
of call is a paramount consideration in the disposition
of a steamship's cargo. But an insight into the old
conditions cannot do any harm and may be found
useful on occasion.

Next I venture to offer the suggestion that the ship should have no auxiliary propulsion of any kind. Let her *be* a sailing ship. I don't exactly know how this may affect the rate of insurance, but I assure you that a very few years ago, well within the life of the man who is addressing you now, nobody thought a sailing ship less safe than a steamship. A ship's safety, apart from the "Act of God," rests in the hands of the men who are aboard of her, from the highest to the lowest in their different degrees. Machinery, *per se*, will not make a ship more safe, and the saved space would be useful for other purposes.

The ship will have, of course, to make use of tugs at the end of her passages. This will afford the cadets an opportunity to get an insight into the various points of seamanship connected with the operations of towage. The mere handling of steel and other kinds of hawsers will by itself give them valuable practice.

General Remarks: Finally I beg leave to touch upon the actual number of people on board. Mr. Laurence Holt's letter speaks of 60 to 80 cadets. I should suggest that the lesser number should be adopted. And even less than 60 if possible. What I have in my mind is the possibility of some accident (which may happen to the best ship afloat) and its effect on the public mind. Regard ought to be paid also to the facility of getting a lesser number of people out of a sinking ship or saving them all in case of a shipwreck.

I have assumed that the period of training would be eighteen months. This in the case of a Conway boy would work out his apprenticeship as follows: One year sea service allowed for Conway training; one year and a half in the sailing ship; the last year and a half as apprentice or cadet in a steamship.

In case of boys joining straight from a school on

H

shore I suppose they would be kept for two and a half years on board the sailing vessel and finish their time in steam.

I don't touch on the point of navigational studies, for which no doubt a provision will be made. I will only remark that the greatest care and accuracy should be required from the cadets acting as assistant officers of the watch (and generally from all senior boys) in keeping the ship's dead reckoning. This is a point of seamanship rather than navigation.

The ship, whether at anchor or alongside the quay, ought to offer that aspect of finished smartness alow and aloft that a training ship should have. It must be remembered that wherever she goes she will be representing the entire maritime community of the Port of Liverpool, employers and employed, shipowners and seamen.

The cadets going ashore on leave should always wear the ship's uniform, unless specifically invited to play games. The ship will no doubt have a football team and a cricket eleven.

A harbour watch (as distinguished from anchor watch), composed of one senior and two junior cadets, should be kept. And, generally, a proper amount of formality should be observed in the ship's routine both at sea and in port. It is conducive to self-respect in all ranks.

THE LOSS OF THE *DALGONAR*

To the Editor of the London *Mercury*

Sɪʀ,

Since you have invited comments from nautical readers on a certain obscure passage in the "True Story"
printed in your September number, I will refer here to
the point raised by Mr. L. C. Gane and to some other
mistakes of minor importance. Not that I think they
matter in the least for your readers, who, in any case,
would have perceived the great quality of the narrative.

The passage queried by Mr. L. C. Gane, quite justifiably, runs as follows:

"At noon wore ship . . . 7 ᴘ. ᴍ. wind and sea
increasing, took in the *mizzen fore upper topsail*. 11
ᴘ. ᴍ. wind and sea still increasing, took in the *mizzen
and main upper topsails*."

The italicized words have, nautically speaking, no
sense; the first four absolutely, the second five in relation to the first statement; since it is obvious that the
mizzen upper topsail could not have been taken in
twice.

These are obviously slips of the pen or errors of trans-
cription. The first statement evidently was meant for:
"Took in the mizzen and fore upper topsails," the word
missing in your text being the "and" after the word
"mizzen." The ship then was carrying her fore-sail,
lower fore-topsail, lower and upper main-topsail and
lower mizzen-topsail. At 11 ᴘ. ᴍ., the gale still increasing, the sails taken in were the "mizzen *lower*

and main upper topsails," the word missing in the phrase as it stands in the text being the word "lower" after the word "mizzen." Thus, at 11 P. M. the ship was reduced down to her foresail and the fore and main lower topsails, which was a possible and seamanlike canvas for her to carry in the then state of the weather. I cannot, however, defend myself from the impression conveyed by the narrative and also from what happened afterwards, that the foresail was carried on her too long. That large piece of canvas must have had the effect (at least at times) of forcing the ship one and a half or perhaps two knots through the water—for no object that I can see. And *there* was the danger. But it is easy to be wise after the event!

The paragraph queried by Mr. Gane contains also a printing error: the plural "s" should come out of the word "foresails." A ship has got only one foresail.

As to other minor corrections, the words "*main draft*" in the opening paragraph of the story should be "*mean draft*," as is obvious from the inspection of the figures. The draught of water is a formal logbook entry in any ship about to proceed to sea. Another misprint (on page 483) consists in a superfluous letter. The line runs: "and *web* squared-in the main and crossjack yards, etc., etc." The "b" got in there by mistake. It should, of course, run: "and *we* squared-in the main, etc.," in what is a correct description of wearing ship, which was the last manœuvre attempted before the *Dalgonar* became unmanageable.

On the next page the meaningless word printed as "nil" should, of course, be "rail."

I agree with all my heart with the editorial note heading the story. There can be nothing finer or more simple. The crew of the *Dalgonar* behaved as well as I have ever seen the crew of a British merchant ship

behave in a critical situation, and they deserve fully
the encomiums and blessings Mr. Mull, the Chief
Officer, gives to them in his report written on board
the *Loire*. A tribute of admiration is due, too, to the
captain of the French ship for his humane determination to save those men, and for the display of seamanlike resolution and skill in maintaining his ship in
position for so long in such desperate weather. Nobody but a seaman can appreciate the risks and the
difficulty of the task, and the severe strain put on the
endurance of the crew and officers of the *Loire* in sheer
physical exertions, in unremitting vigilance and plucky
seamanship, which enabled them to remain by and
finally to take off the crew of the *Dalgonar*.

Yours, etc.,

JOSEPH CONRAD.

TRAVEL

A Preface to Richard Curle's "Into the East"

There is no fate so uncertain as the fate of books of travel. They are the most assailable of all men's literary productions. The man who writes a travel book delivers himself more than any other into the hands of his enemies. The popularizing scientific writer's position is much more secure. His very subject is, properly speaking, marvellous in itself, and for that reason the intelligent multitude swallows it eagerly, or at least receives it with open mouth, and forms its own amazing conclusions. A writer of fiction—well!—he romances all the time, and the truth he has in him being disguised in various garments, from gold mantles to rags, is almost beyond the reach of criticism. All really he has got to attend to is grammar and punctuation. Metaphysics, of course, are simply intoxicating for those who like that way of killing our appointed time in this valley of tears. But as to those whose fancy leads them to investigate more or less profoundly that same valley. . . !

But after all a traveller is very much to be envied. He is to be envied for the instinct that prompts him, for the courage that sustains him. He is to be admired for enduring a spectacle almost intolerably gorgeous and varied, but with only hints, here and there, of dramatic scenes, with, practically, no star actors in it, with the knowledge that the curtain will not fall for months and months to come; and that he must play the

exacting part of a spectator of those human characteristics and activities, in their picturesque, ugly, or savage
settings, without, so to speak, the prospect of going
home to bed presently. Imagine a lover of drama and
of stage effects forced to sleep in his very stall, and every
day, opening his eyes upon a never-ceasing performance. The taste for that sort of thing may well be
envied as evidence of capacity for mental and physical
resistance, not only against the strain of all the "things
that seem to be," but against one's own weakness.
Perhaps that is the reason why the Arabs, racially
great travellers and great lovers of wonders, invented
the proverb, "Travelling is victory," which stands
as the motto of this book. It expresses, indeed, a
romantic conception. But there is a soberness of
temperament in the Arab race which has prevented it
from rushing exultingly into the writing of travel
books. Of course, I am an ignorant person, from
circumstances which it would not be to my advantage
to disclose, but I can only call to mind one Arab
traveller who has written a book; and surely if there
had been shoals of them I would have heard of another.

Those people did much of their travelling sword in
hand and with the name of the One God on their lips.
But theirs were personally conducted parties, as
destructive to the peace and the spiritual character of
places they visited as any crowd from a tourist agency
invading the shades of Vallombrosa. Let us forget the
Arabs as well as their successors who are achieving
victory every year at the price of so many pounds per
head for a certain number of days. They demand
neither our admiration nor our pity.

Nowadays many people encompass the globe. That
kind of victory became to a certain extent fashionable
for some years after the piercing of the Isthmus of

Suez. Multitudes rushed through that short cut with blank minds and, alas, also blank notebooks where the megalomania, from which we all more or less suffer, got recorded in the shape of "Impressions." The inanity of the mass of travel books the Suez Canal is responsible for took the proportions of an enormous and melancholy joke. For it was a mournful sight to see so many people giving themselves away. Their books covered private shelves and the tables of *cabinets de lecture* in a swarm more devastating to the world's freshness of impression than a swarm of locusts in a field of young corn. When that visitation began I was quite a boy and in my innocence I read them all, or, at least, all I could lay my hands on. Women, single or in pairs, fashionable couples, professors of intense gravity, facetious business men—I read all their travel books, including even Baron Hübner's "Voyage Round the World," which, I should think, remains unequalled to this day.

That category of travellers with their parrot-like remarks, their strange attempts at being funny, and their lamentable essays in seriousness has apparently passed away. Or perhaps they only print their books for circulation amongst friends. I suspect, however, they have ceased to write simply because there are too many of them. They do not appear as travellers even to the most naïve minds and perhaps even to their own minds. They are simply an enormous company of people who go round the world for a change and rest, either suffering from overwork (whatever that may mean) or from neurasthenia. And I am sure my best wishes go with them for an easy and radical recovery. Steamship companies love them.

Sporting travellers form a class by themselves. They mostly write for other sportsmen, though I must confess that their books hold for me even now some fascination. They are apt to grow monotonous in the descriptive statistics of slaughter and as to the shortcomings of their "boys." Also in their admiration for their trackers, who seem all to have been made from the same pattern. I have noticed them adopting of late years a half-apologetic tone about their exploits; whereas the men of twenty-five years ago, with their much less perfect weapons and their big records, were frankly exulting. Frankness is a virtue I like. I would respect the modern attitude more if I were sure of its absolute genuineness. Moderation in game killing is enforced now by many regulations; but on considering how easy it is not to shoot an antelope one becomes slightly doubtful of the perfect candour of men who travel thousands of miles in dreary steamboats and uncomfortable primitive trains for sport. On the other hand, I admit that a sportsman who would consistently miss every antelope would be an extremely uninteresting person. The world of explorers and discoverers, the heroes of my boyhood, has vanished almost to nothing in the nineteenth century. Some of them wrote the classics of travel, but no passage of years can dim my admiration for their selfless spirit and manly faithfulness to their task pursued in solitude or with a few devoted henchmen, persevered in through numberless days with death only a pace behind, but with a calm mind and a steady heart.

What about mere wanderers?—those individuals that one meets in various fairly well-known localities, but who come upon one round unexpected corners, often shabby and depressed, sometimes haggard and jaunty; with tales in their mouths of the flattest description or of a comic quality bordering on tears; with, now and then, a story that would frighten you to death if

*H

you were one of those men who don't know how to smile in time. I would class them as an outcast tribe if it did not sound so rude. And I would not be rude for anything to people capable of starting on their travels with their hands, and very little else besides, in their pockets. I have known amongst them men of ruffianly mental complexion, cultivating a truculent manner and a cold steady stare, who, if it were possible to bluff one's own destiny, might have been sitting in high places. And I ask myself, in my half-reluctant partiality for the class, whether some of them have not achieved it. But success disguises them at once and contemporary history gives them other names.

In my review of the categories of men who move about the earth I come now to the real travellers who wrote books, the protagonists of the modern travellers, in the same way, I may say, in which Hannon may be looked upon as a protagonist of the discoverers and the circumnavigators of the globe. Only the *Periplus* was probably a dreary official report. At any rate it has not come down to us. The outstanding figure amongst those men who dedicated their books of travel to popes and emperors is Marco Polo, with his meticulous descriptive gift, his cautious credulity, his eye for splendour and his historian's rather than a traveller's temperament. He gave his readers what the readers of that day wanted, historical facts in a foreign and gorgeous atmosphere. But the time for such books of travel is past on this earth girt about with cables, with an atmosphere made restless by the waves of ether, lighted by that sun of the twentieth century under which there is nothing new left now, and but very little of what may still be called obscure.

The day of many-volumed "Journeys, through or to," of "Relations of this or that" (and much charm and ability some of them had), the days of heroic travel are gone; unless, of course, in the newspaper sense, in which heroism like everything else in the world becomes as common if not as nourishing as our daily bread.   There would be always a lady or a gentleman ready to discover with considerable fuss a bit of territory of, say, ten square miles, resembling exactly the surrounding and already explored lands; or interview some new ruler, like a reflection in a dim and tarnished mirror of some real chieftain in the books of a hundred years ago; or marvel at a disagreeable fish of ferocious habits which had been described already in some old-time, simply worded, unsensational "Relation." But even this is a game which is losing its interest, and in a very little time will have come to an end.   Presently there will be no backyard left in the heart of Central Africa that has not been peeped into by some person more or less commissioned for the purpose.   The Nigeria of Barth, of Denham, of Clapperton, of Mungo Park, of other infinitely curious and profoundly inspired men, will be bristling with police posts, colleges, tramway poles, and all those improving things triumphantly recorded, and always with the romantic addition that, within twenty miles, the hills, or the forests, or the holes in the sand, or the depths of the jungle (that blessed word) are swarming with cannibal tribes miraculously restrained by one white man with two black soldiers and his native cook for all company. And the great cloud of fatuous daily photographs and even more fatuous descriptive chatter, under whose shadow no traveller could live, will brood over those seldom-visited places of the world that, despoiled of their old black soul of mystery, have not yet acquired its substitute, which will be marvellously piebald when it comes.

This moment of ill-humour with "things as they are becoming" is of course perfectly unreasonable and even perverse, which is worse. It would not deserve to be tolerated except for its inherent piety. As a matter of fact I have been thinking for a moment of the dead, of the great and good travellers loved in my boyhood, as I laid aside the MS. of this modern traveller who by publishing it has delivered himself to his enemies. He is very modern, for he is fashioned by the conditions of an explored earth in which the latitudes and longitudes having been recorded once for all have become things of no importance, in the sense that they can no longer appeal to the spirit of adventure, inflame no imagination, lead no one up to the very gates of mortal danger.

These basic facts of geography having been ascertained by the observations of heavenly bodies, the glance of the modern traveller contemplating the much-surveyed earth beholds in fact a world in a state of transition; very different in this from the writers of travel books of Marco Polo's time, who in their conscientious narratives seem to progress amongst immutable wonders, to feed their curiosity on a consistency of the splendid and the bizarre, presented to their eyes to stare at, to their minds to moralize upon.

And those things, which stand as if imperishable in the pages of old books of travel, are all blown away, have vanished as utterly as the smoke of the travellers' camp fires in the icy night air of the Gobi Desert, as the smell of incense burned in the temples of strange gods, as the voices of Asiatic statesmen speculating with the cruel wisdom of past ages on matters of peace and war.

Nothing obviously strange remains for our eyes now. The Khan of Tartary's court ceremonies were certainly marvellous in quite a different sense from the procedure followed at Kuala Kangsar two years ago, when the Sultan of Perak was invested with the K. C. M. G. by the Governor of the Straits Settlements. This modern traveller describes it all in less words than Marco Polo would have used paragraphs on such a striking occasion. It was curious for him to watch under the formal routine of official compliments the Malay princes play up to British etiquette, while grafting it on their own ideas of politeness, and wearing, he thought, a slightly ironical smile on their dark faces. And to think that only fifty years ago, after a certain amount of jungle and stockade fighting, the Sultan of Perak, or perhaps his brother ruler next door in Selangor, having listened attentively to a lecture from a British Admiral on the heinousness of a certain notable case of piracy, turned round quickly to his attending chiefs and to the silent throng of his Malay subjects, exclaiming, "Hear now, my people! Don't let us have any more of this little game." Those words ought to have been engraved in letters of gold on a marble monument at the mouth of the Jugra River; for from the moment they were pronounced dates the era of security for the poor folks of the coast, for the fishermen and traders in the Straits of Malacca. The downfall of local piracy in fact. The world in transition!

Our very curiosities have changed, growing more subtle amongst the vanishing mysteries of the earth. Very appropriately this modern traveller reclining on the verandah of the State Rest-house, after having watched the ceremonies of installation in the blaring of trumpets and the gorgeous bright colours of the throng, recalls the strong impression of, one might say, indifferent and rather contemptuous good-will between brown and white, and gives himself up to the vain (as he himself observes) occupation of speculating on the

future of countries. But he does it not in the spirit of
a statesman looking for political truth, but in the doubt-
ing mood of a traveller of our day who on the very
threshold of the East has questioned himself as to the
ultimate truth of travel; whether perchance it was no
more than the mastery of first impressions; and whether
the sanity of our outlook on the world consists in secret
revolt against its facts but in the final acceptance of the
whole, or in the conformity with all the multiple forms
and the mental rejection of life's inscrutable purpose?
It is this mood which makes him so responsive to the
inner promptings suggested by travel, which informs
the felicitous rendering of his visual impressions. This
it is that forces him, while looking out into the night
from the deck of an Irrawaddy flotilla steamer, to
admit to himself man's secret antagonism to the wilderness; or during his few hours' stay in Bhamo, a town
on the very frontier of the Chinese enigma, where
caravans incessantly come and go through mysterious
valleys and where people live on rumours from day to
day, to absorb its spirit of secrecy and waiting and hear
suddenly around him "the whisper of innumerable
hills passing on one to another the restless murmur of
men's hearts." Very modern in impressions, in appreci-
ations, in curiosities, and in his very love of the mother
earth, of whose children he has written subtly and
tenderly in some three volumes of characteristic tales;
a traveller of our day, condemned to make his discoveries on beaten tracks, he looks on, sensitive,
meditative, with delicate perceptions and a gift for
expression, alive to the saving grace of human and
historical associations; and while pursuing amongst
the men busy with ascertained facts the riddles presented by a world in transition, he seems to have
captured for us the spirit of modern travel itself.

STEPHEN CRANE

A Preface to Thomas Beer's "Stephen Crane"

On a rainy day of March of the year 1923, listening to the author of this biography telling me of his earnest labours for the memory of a man who was certainly unique in his generation, I exclaimed to myself with wonder: "And so it has come to pass after all—this thing which I did not expect to see!" In truth I had never expected the biography of Stephen Crane to appear in my lifetime. My immense pleasure was affected by the devastating touch of time which like a muddy flood covers under a mass of daily trivialities things of value: moments of affectionate communion with kindred spirits, words spoken with the careless freedom of perfect confidence, the deepest emotions of joy and sorrow—together with such things of merely historical importance as the recollection of dates, for instance. After hearing from Mr. Beer of his difficulties in fixing certain dates in the history of Stephen Crane's life, I discovered that I was unable to remember with any kind of precision the initial date of our friendship. Indeed, life is but a dream—especially for those of us who have never kept a diary or possessed a notebook in our lives.

In this extremity I had recourse to another friend of Stephen Crane, who had appreciated him intuitively almost as soon as I did myself and who is a woman of excellent memory. My wife's recollection is that Crane and I met in London in October, 1897, and that he came

93

to see us for the first time in our Essex home in the following November.

I have mentioned in a short paper written two years ago that it was Mr. S. S. Pawling, partner in the publishing firm of Mr. Heinemann, who brought us together. It was done at Stephen Crane's own desire.

I was told by Mr. Pawling that when asked whom he wanted to meet Crane mentioned two names, of which one was of a notable journalist (who had written some novels) whom he knew in America, I believe, and the other was mine. At that time the only facts we knew about each other were that we both had the same publisher in England. The only other fact I knew about Stephen Crane was that he was quite a young man. I had, of course, read his "Red Badge of Courage," of which people were writing and talking at that time. I certainly did not know that he had the slightest notion of my existence, or that he had seen a single line (there were not many of them then) of my writing. I can safely say that I earned this precious friendship by something like ten months of strenuous work with my pen. It took me just that time to write "The Nigger of the *Narcissus*," working at what I always considered a very high pressure. It was on the ground of the authorship of that book that Crane wanted to meet me. Nothing could have been more flattering than to discover that the author of "The Red Badge of Courage" appreciated my effort to present a group of men held together by a common loyalty and a common perplexity in a struggle not with human enemies, but with the hostile conditions testing their faithfulness to the conditions of their own calling.

Apart from the imaginative analysis of his own temperament tried by the emotions of a battlefield,

Stephen Crane dealt in his book with the psychology of the mass—the army; while I—in mine—had been dealing with the same subject on a much smaller scale and in more specialized conditions—the crew of a merchant ship, brought to the test of what I may venture to call the moral problem of conduct. This may be thought a very remote connection between these two works and the idea may seem too far-fetched to be mentioned here; but that was my undoubted feeling at the time. It is a fact that I considered Crane, by virtue of his creative experience with "The Red Badge of Courage," as eminently fit to pronounce a judgment on my first consciously planned attempt to render the truth of a phase of life in the terms of my own temperament with all the sincerity of which I was capable.

I had, of course, my own opinion as to what I had done; but I doubted whether anything of my ambitiously comprehensive aim would be understood. I was wrong there; but my doubt was excusable, since I myself would have been hard put to it if requested to give my complex intentions the form of a concise and definite statement. In that period of misgivings which so often follows an accomplished task I would often ask myself, who in the world could be interested in such a thing? It was after reading "The Red Badge," which came into my hands directly after its publication in England, that I said to myself: "Here's a man who may understand—if he ever sees the book; though of course that would not mean that he would like it." I do not mean to say that I looked towards the author of "The Red Badge" as the only man in the world. It would have been stupid and ungrateful. I had the moral support of one or two intimate friends and the solid fact of Mr. W. E. Henley's acceptance of my tale for serial publication in the *New Review* to give me confidence, while I awaited the larger verdict.

It seems to me that in trying to recall my memories of Stephen Crane I have been talking so far only about myself; but that is unavoidable, since this Introduction, which I am privileged to write, can only trace what is left on earth of our personal intercourse, which was even more short and fleeting than it may appear from the record of dates. October, 1897—May, 1900. And out of that beggarly tale of months must be deducted the time of his absence from England during the Spanish-American War, and of his visit to the United States shortly before the beginning of his last illness. Even when he was in England our intercourse was not so close and frequent as the warmth of our friendship would have wished it to be. We both lived in the country and, though not very far from each other, in different counties. I had my work to do, always in conditions which made it a matter of urgency. He had his own tasks and his own visions to attend to. I do not think that he had more friendships to claim him than I, but he certainly had more acquaintances and more calls on his time.

This was only natural. It must be remembered that as an author he was my senior, as I used to remind him now and then with affected humility which always provoked his smiles. He had a quiet smile that charmed and frightened one. It made you pause by something revelatory it cast over his whole physiognomy, not like a ray but like a shadow. I often asked myself what it could be, that quality that checked one's care-free mood, and now I think I have had my answer. It was the smile of a man who knows that his time will not be long on this earth.

I would not for a moment wish to convey the impression of melancholy in connection with my memories of Stephen Crane. I saw his smile first over the tablecloth in a restaurant. We shook hands with intense gravity and a direct stare at each other, after the manner of two children told to make friends. It was under the encouraging gaze of Sydney Pawling, who, a much bigger man than either of us and possessed of a deep voice, looked like a grown-up person entertaining two strange small boys—protecting and slightly anxious as to the experiment. He knew very little of either of us. I was a new author and Crane was a new arrival. It was the meeting of "The Red Badge" and "The Nigger" in the presence of their publisher; but as far as our personalities went we were three strangers breaking bread together for the first time. Yet it was as pleasantly easy a meal as any I can remember. Crane talked in his characteristic deliberate manner about Greece at war. I had already sensed the man's intense earnestness underlying his quiet surface. Every time he raised his eyes, that secret quality (for his voice was careless) of his soul was betrayed in a clear flash. Most of the true Stephen Crane was in his eyes, most of his strength at any rate, though it was apparent also in his other features, as, for instance, in the structure of his forehead, the deep solid arches under the fair eyebrows.

Some people saw traces of weakness in the lower part of his face. What I could see there was a hint of the delicacy of sentiment, of the inborn fineness of nature which this man, whose life had been anything but a stroll through a rose-garden, had managed to preserve like a sacred heritage. I say heritage, not acquisition, for it was not and could not have been acquired. One could depend on it on all occasions; whereas the cultivated kind is apt to show ugly gaps under very slight provocation. The coarseness of the professedly delicate must be very amusing to the misanthrope. But Crane was no enemy of his kind. That sort of thing did not amuse him. As to his own temper, it was proof against anger and scorn, as I can testify, having seen him both angry and scornful, always quietly, on fitting occasions. Contempt and indignation never broke the surface of his moderation, simply because he had no surface. He was all through of the same material, incapable of affectation of any kind, of any pitiful failure of generosity for the sake of personal advantage, or even from sheer exasperation which must find its relief.

Many people imagined him a fiery individuality. Certainly he was not cold-blooded. But his was an equable glow, morally and temperamentally. I would have said the same of his creative power (I have seen him sit down before a blank sheet of paper, dip his pen, write the first line at once and go on without haste and without pause for a couple of hours), had he not confided to me that his mentality did flag at times. I do not think it was anything more than every writer is familiar with at times. Another man would have talked of his "failing inspiration." It is very characteristic of Crane that I have never heard him use that word when talking about his work.

His phraseology was generally of a very modest cast. That unique and exquisite faculty, which Edward Garnett, another of his friends, found in his writing— "of disclosing an individual scene by an odd simile"— was not apparent in his conversation. It was interesting, of course, but its charm consisted mainly in the freshness of his impressions, set off by an acute simplicity of view and expressed with an amusing deliberation. Superabundance of words was not his failing when communing with those he liked and felt he could trust. With the other kind of "friends" he followed the method of a sort of suspended silence. On a certain occasion (it was at Brede Place), after two amazingly conceited idiots had gone away, I said to him, "Stevie, you brood like a distant thundercloud." He had retired early to the other end of the room, and from there had sent out, now and then, a few words, more like the heavy drops of rain that precede the storm than growls of thunder. Poor Crane, if he could look black enough at times, never thundered; though I have no doubt he could have been dangerous if he had liked. There always seemed to be something (not timidity) which restrained him, not from within but, I could not help fancying, from outside, with an effect as of a whispered *memento mori* in the ear of a reveller not lost to the sense of grace.

That of course was a later impression. It must be stated clearly that I know very little of Stephen Crane's life. We did not feel the need to tell each other formally the story of our lives. That did not prevent us from being very intimate and also very open with each other from the first. Our affection would have been "everlasting," as he himself qualified it, had not the jealous death intervened with her cruel capriciousness by striking down the younger man. Our intimacy was really too close to admit of indiscretions; not that he did not speak amusingly of his experiences and of his hardships, and warmly of the men that helped him in his early days, like Mr. Hamlin Garland for instance, or men kindly encouraging to him, like Mr. Howells. Many other names he used to utter lovingly have been forgotten by me after so many years.

It is a fact that I heard more of his adventures than of his trials, privations, and difficulties. I know he had many. He was the least recriminatory of men (though one of the most sensitive, I should say), but, in any case, nothing I could have learned would have shaken the independent judgment I had formed for myself of his trustworthiness as a man and a friend. Though the word is discredited now and may sound pretentious, I will say that there was in Crane a strain of chivalry which made him safe to trust with one's life. To be recognizably a man of honour carries no immunity against human weaknesses, but comports more rigid limitations in personal relations than the status of an "honourable man," however recognizable that too may be. Some men are "honourable" by courtesy, others by the office they hold, or simply by belonging to some popular assembly, the election to which is not generally secured by a dignified accuracy of statement and a scrupulous regard for the feelings of others. Many remain honourable (because of their great circumspection in the conduct of their affairs) without holding within themselves any of these restraints which are inherent in the character of a man of honour, however weak or luckless he may be.

I do not know everything about the strength of Crane's circumspection, but I am not afraid of what the biography which follows may disclose to us; though I am convinced that it will be free from hypocritical reservations. I think I have understood Stephen Crane, and from my too short acquaintance with his biographer I am confident he will receive the most humane and sympathetic treatment. What I discovered very early in our acquaintance was that Crane had not the face of a lucky man. That certitude came to me at our first meeting while I sat opposite him listening to his simple tales of Greece, while S. S. Pawling presided at the initiatory feast—friendly and debonair, looking solidly anchored in the stream of life, and very reassuring, like a big, prosperous ship to the sides of which we two in our tossing little barks could hook on for safety. He was interested in the tales too; and the best proof of it is that when he looked at his watch and jumped up, saying, "I must leave you two now," it was very near four o'clock. Nearly a whole afternoon wasted, for an English business man.

No such consideration of waste or duty agitated Crane and myself. The sympathy that, even in regard of the very few years allotted to our friendship, may be said to have sprung up instantaneously between us, was the most undemonstrative case of that sort in the last century. We not only did not tell each other of it (which would have been missish), but even without entering formally into a previous agreement to remain together, we went out and began to walk side by side in the manner of two tramps without home, occupation, or care for the next night's shelter. We certainly paid no heed to direction. The first thing I noticed were the Green Park railings, when to my remark that he had seen no war before he went to Greece, Crane made answer: "No. But 'The Red Badge' is all right." I assured him that I never had doubted it; and, since the title of the work had been pronounced for the first time, feeling I must do something to show I had read it, I said shyly: "I like your General." He knew at once what I was alluding to, but said not a word. Nothing could have been more tramp-like than our silent pacing, elbow to elbow, till, after we had left Hyde Park Corner behind us, Crane uttered with his quiet earnestness the words: "I like your young man— I can just see him." Nothing could have been more characteristic of the depth of our three-hour-old intimacy than that each of us should have selected for praise the merest by-the-way vignette of a minor character.

This was positively the only allusion we made that afternoon to our immortal works. Indeed we talked very little of them at any time, and then always selecting some minor point for particular mention; which, after all, is not a bad way of showing an affectionate appreciation of a piece of work done by a friend. A stranger would have expected more, but, in a manner of speaking, Crane and I had never been strangers. We took each other's work for granted from the very first, I mean from the moment we had exchanged those laudatory remarks alongside the Green Park railings. Henceforth mutual recognition kept to that standard. It consisted often of an approving grunt, sometimes of the mention of some picked-out paragraph, or of a line or only of a few words that had caught our fancy and would, for a time, be applied more or less aptly to the turns of our careless, or even serious, talks.

Thus, for instance, there was a time when I persecuted poor Crane with the words "barbarously abrupt." They occur in that marvellous story, "The Open Boat", and are applied by him to the waves of the sea (as seen by men tossing in a small dinghy) with an inspired audacity of epithet which was one of Crane's gifts that gave me most delight. How amazingly apt these words are where they stand, anybody can see by looking at that story, which is altogether a big thing, and has remained an object of my confirmed admiration. I was always telling Crane that this or that was "barbarously abrupt," or begging him not to be so "barbarously abrupt" himself, with a keen enjoyment of the incongruity; for no human being could be less abrupt than Crane. As to his humanity (in contradistinction to barbarity), it was a shining thing without a flaw. It is possible that he may have grown at length weary of my little joke, but he invariably received it with a smile, thus proving his consistent humanity towards his kind. But, after all, he too liked that story of his, of four men in a very small boat, which by the deep and simple humanity of presentation seems somehow to illustrate the essentials of life itself, like a symbolic tale. It opens with a phrase that anybody could have uttered, but which, in relation to what is to follow, acquires the poignancy of a meaning almost universal. Once, much later in our acquaintance, I made use of it to him. He came on a flying visit to Pent Farm where we were living then. I noticed that he looked harassed. I, too, was feeling for the moment as if things were getting too much for me. He lay on the couch and I sat on a chair opposite. After a longish silence, in which we both could have felt how uncertain was the issue of life envisaged as a deadly adventure in which we were both engaged like two men trying to keep afloat in a small boat, I said suddenly across the width of the mantelpiece:

"None of them knew the colour of the sky."

He raised himself sharply. The words had struck him as familiar, though I believe he failed to place them at first. "Don't you know that quotation?" I asked. (These words form the opening sentence of his tale.) The startled expression passed off his face. "Oh, yes," he said quietly, and lay down again. Truth to say, it was a time when neither he nor I had the leisure to look up idly at the sky. The waves just then were too "barbarously abrupt."

I do not mean to say that it was always so. Now and then we were permitted to snatch a glance at the colour of the sky. But it is a fact that in the history of our essentially undemonstrative friendship (which is nearly as difficult to recapture as a dream) that first long afternoon is the most care-free instant, and the only one that had a character of enchantment about it. It was spread out over a large portion of central London. After the Green Park the next thing I remember are the Kensington Gardens, where under the lofty and historical trees I was vouchsafed a glimpse of the low mesquite bush overspreading the plum-coloured infinities of the great Texas plains. Then after a long tramp amongst an orderly multitude of grimy brick houses—from which the only things I carried off were the impressions of the coloured rocks of Mexico (or was it Arizona?), and my first knowledge of a locality called the Painted Desert—there came suddenly Oxford Street. I don't know whether the inhabitants of London were keeping indoors or had gone into the country that afternoon, but I don't remember seeing any people in the streets except for a figure, now and then, unreal, flitting by, obviously negligible. The wheeled traffic, too, was stopped; yet, it seems, not entirely, because I remember Crane seizing my arm and jerking me back on the pavement with the calm remark: "You will get run over." I love to think that the dear fellow had saved my life and that it seemed to amuse him. As to London's enormous volume of business, all I know is that one A. B. C. shop had remained open. We went through the depressing ceremony of having tea there; but our interest in each other mitigated its inherent horrors and gave me a good idea of Crane's stoicism. At least I suppose we had tea, otherwise they would not have let us sit there so long. To be left alone was all we wanted. Neither of us had then a club to entertain the other in. It will give a good notion of our indomitable optimism (on that afternoon) when I say that it was there, in those dismal surroundings, we reached the conclusion that though the world had grown old and weary, yet the scheme of creation remained as obscure as ever, and (from our own particular point of view) there was still much that was interesting to expect from gods and men.

As if intoxicated by this draught of hope we rolled out of that A. B. C. shop, but I kept my head sufficiently to guess what was coming and to send a warning telegram to my wife in our Essex home. Crane then was, I believe, staying temporarily in London. But he seemed to have no care in the world; and so we resumed our tramping—east and north and south again, steering through uncharted mazes the streets, forgetting to think of dinner but taking a rest here and there, till we found ourselves, standing in the middle of Piccadilly Circus, blinking at the lights like two authentic night-birds. By that time we had been (in Tottenham Court Road) joined by Balzac. How he came in I have no idea. Crane was not given to literary curiosities of that kind. Somebody he knew, or something he had read, must have attracted lately his attention to Balzac. And now suddenly at ten o'clock in the evening he demanded insistently to be told in particular detail all about the "Comédie Humaine," its contents, its scope, its plan, and its general significance, together with a critical description of Balzac's style. I told him hastily that it was just black on white; and for the rest, I said, he would have to wait till we got across to Monico's and had eaten some supper. I hoped he would forget Balzac and his "Comédie." But not a bit of it; and I had no option but to hold forth over the remnants of a meal, in the rush of hundreds of waiters and the clatter of tons of crockery, caring not what I said (for what could Stephen want with Balzac?), in the comfortable assurance that the Monstrous Shade, even if led by some strange caprice to haunt the long room of Monico's, did not know enough English to understand a single word I said. I wonder what Crane made of it all. He did not look bored, and it was eleven o'clock before we parted at the foot of that monumentally heavy abode of frivolity, the Pavilion, with just a hand-shake and a good-night—no more—without making any arrangements for meeting again, as though we had lived in the same town from childhood and were sure to run across each other next day.

It struck me directly I left him that we had not even exchanged addresses; but I was not uneasy. Sure enough, before the month was out there arrived a post card (from Ravensbrook) asking whether he might come to see us. He came, was received as an old friend, and before the end of the day conquered my wife's sympathy, as undemonstrative and sincere as his own quiet friendliness. The friendship that sprang up between them was confirmed by the interest Crane displayed in our first child, a boy who came on the scene not quite two months afterwards. How strong was that interest on the part of Stephen Crane and his wife in the boy is evidenced by the fact that at the age of six weeks he was invited to come for a long visit to Ravensbrook. He was in fact impatiently expected there. He arrived in state, bringing with him not only his parents but also a young aunt, and was welcomed like a prince. This visit, during which I suffered from a sense of temporary extinction, is commemorated by a group photograph taken by an artist summoned with his engine (regardless of expense) to Ravensbrook. Though the likenesses are not bad, it is a very awful thing. Nobody looks like him or herself in it. The best yet are the Crane dogs, a very important part of the establishment and quite conscious of it, belonging apparently to some order of outlandish poodles, amazingly sedate, and yet the most restless animals I have ever met. They pervaded, populated, and filled the whole house. Whichever way one looked at any time, down the passage, up the stairs, into the drawing room, there was always a dog in sight. Had I been asked on the first day how many there were, I would have guessed about thirty. As a matter of fact there were only three, but I think they never sat down, except in Crane's study, where they had their *entrée* at all hours.

A scratching would be heard at the door, Crane would drop his pen with alacrity to throw it open—and the dogs would enter sedately in single file, taking a lot of time about it, too. Then the room would resound for a while with grunts, sniffs, yawns, heavy flops, followed by as much perhaps as three whole minutes of silence. Then the dogs would get up, one after another, never all together, and direct their footsteps to the door in an impressive and ominous manner. The first arrival waited considerately for the others before trying to attract attention by means of scratching on the bottom panel. Then, never before, Crane would raise his head, go meekly to the door—and the procession would file out at the slowest possible pace. The recurrent sedateness of the proceedings, the utter unconsciousness of the dogs, dear Stephen's absurd gravity while playing his part in those ceremonies, without ever a muscle of his face moving, were irresistibly, exasperatingly funny. I tried to preserve my gravity (or at least to keep calm), with fair success. Only one afternoon on the fifth or sixth repetition I could not help bursting into a loud interminable laugh, and then the dear fellow asked me in all innocence what was the matter. I managed to conceal my nervous irritation from him, and he never learned the secret of that laugh in which there was a beginning of hysteria.

If the definition that man is a laughing animal be true, then Crane was neither one nor the other; indeed he was but a hurried visitor on this earth on which he had so little reason to be joyous. I might say that I never heard him laugh, except in connection with the baby. He loved children; but his friendship with our child was of the kind that put our mutual sentiment, by comparison, somewhere within the arctic region. The two could not be compared; at least I have never detected Crane stretched full length and sustained on his elbows on a grass plot, in order to gaze at me; on the other hand, this was his usual attitude of communion with the small child—with him who was called *the Boy* and whose destiny it was to see more war before he came of age than the author of "The Red Badge" had time to see in all the allotted days of his life. In the gravity of its disposition the baby came quite up to Crane; yet those two would sometimes find something to laugh at in each other. Then there would be silence, and glancing out of the low window of my room I would see them, very still, staring at each other with a solemn understanding that needed no words, or perhaps was beyond words altogether. I could not object on any ground to their profound intimacy, but I do not see why Crane should have developed such an unreasonable suspicion as to my paternal efficiency. He seemed to be everlastingly taking the boy's part. I could not see that the baby was being oppressed, hectored over, or in any way deprived of its rights, or ever wounded in its feelings by me; but Crane seemed always to nurse some vague unexpressed grievance as to my conduct. I was inconsiderate. For instance—why could I not get a dog for the boy? One day he made quite a scene about it. He seemed to imply I should drop everything and go look for a dog. I sat under the storm and said nothing. At last he cried, "Hang it all, a boy ought to have a dog." It was an appeal to first principles, but for an answer I pointed at the window and said: "Behold the boy." . . . He was sitting on a rug spread on the grass, with his little red stocking-cap very much over one eye (a fact of which he seemed unaware), and propped round with many pillows on account of his propensity to roll over on his side helplessly. My answer was irresistible. This is one of the few occasions on which I heard Stephen Crane laugh outright. He dropped his preaching on the dog theme and went out to the boy while I went on with my work. But he was strangely incorrigible. When he came back after an hour or so, his first words were, "Joseph, I will teach your boy to ride." I closed with the offer at once—but it was not to be. He was not given the time.

The happiest mental picture my wife and I preserve of Crane is on the occasion of our first visit to Brede Place when he rode to meet us at the Park gate. He looked at his best on horseback. On that day he must have been feeling well. As usual, he was happy in the saddle. As he went on trotting by the side of the open trap I said to him: "If you give the boy your seat I will be perfectly satisfied." I knew this would please him; and indeed his face remained wreathed in smiles all the way to the front door. He looked about him at that bit of the world, down the green slopes and up the brown fields, with an appreciative serenity and the confident bearing of a man who is feeling very sure of the present and of the future. All because he was looking at life from the saddle, with a good morning's work behind him. Nothing more is needed to give a man a blessed moment of illusion. The more I think

of that morning, the more I believe it was just that; that
it had really been given me to see Crane perfectly happy
for a couple of hours; and that it was under this spell
that directly we arrived he led me impatiently to the
room in which he worked when at Brede. After we got
there he said to me, "Joseph, I will give you something." I had no idea what it would be, till I saw him
sit down to write an inscription in a very slim volume.
He presented it to me with averted head. It was "The
Black Riders." He had never spoken to me of his
verse before. It was while holding the book in my
hand that I learned that they were written years before
in America. I expressed my appreciation of them that
afternoon in the usual half-a-dozen, or dozen, words
which we allowed ourselves when completely pleased
with each other's work. When the pleasure was not
so complete the words would be many. And that was
a great waste of breath and time. I must confess that
we were no critics, I mean temperamentally. Crane
was even less of a critic than myself. Criticism is very
much a matter of a vocabulary, very consciously used;
with us it was the intonation that mattered. The tone
of a grunt could convey an infinity of meaning between
us.

The articulate literary conscience at our elbow was
Edward Garnett. He, of course, was worth listening
to. His analytical appreciation (or appreciative analysis) of Crane's art, in the London *Academy* of 17th
December, 1898,[1] goes to the root of the matter with
Edward's almost uncanny insight, and a well-balanced
sympathy with the blind, pathetic striving of the artist
towards a complete realization of his individual gift.
How highly Edward Garnett rated Crane's gift is
recorded in the conclusions of that admirable and,

[1] Extended and republished in the volume "Friday Nights."

within the limits of its space, masterly article of some
two columns, where at the end are set down such
affirmative phrases as: "The chief impressionist of the
age." . . . "Mr. Crane's talent is unique" . . .
and where he hails him as "the creator of fresh rhythms
and phrases," while the very last words state confidently
that: "Undoubtedly, of the young school it is Mr. Crane
who is the genius—the others have their talents."

My part here being not that of critic but of private
friend, all I will say is that I agreed warmly at the
time with that article, which from the quoted phrases
might be supposed a merely enthusiastic pronounce-
ment, but on reading will be found to be based on that
calm sagacity which Edward Garnett, for all his fiery
zeal in the cause of letters, could always summon for the
judgment of matters emotional—as all response to the
various forms of art must be in the main. I had
occasion to re-read it last year in its expanded form in a
collection of literary essays of great, now almost historical, interest in the record of American and English
imaginative literature. I found there a passage or two,
not bearing precisely on Crane's work but giving a view
of his temperament, on which of course his art was
based; and of the conditions, moral and material, under
which he had to put forth his creative faculties and his
power of steady composition. Of those matters, as a
man who had the opportunity to look at Crane's life
in England, I wish to offer a few remarks before closing
my contribution to the memory of my friend.

I do not know that he was ever dunned for money
and had to work under a threat of legal proceedings.
I don't think he was ever dunned in the sense in which
such a phrase is used about a spendthrift unscrupulous
in incurring debts. No doubt he was sometimes pressed

I

for money. He lived by his pen, and the prices he obtained were not great. Personally he was not extravagant; and I will not quarrel with him for not choosing to live in a garret. The tenancy of Brede Place was held by him at a nominal rent. That glorious old place was not restored then, and the greatest part of it was uninhabitable. The Cranes had furnished in a modest way six or seven of the least dilapidated rooms, which even then looked bare and half empty. Certainly there was a horse, and at one time even two, but that luxury was not so very expensive at that time. One man looked after them. Riding was the only exercise open to Crane; and if he did work so hard, surely he was entitled to some relaxation, if only for the preservation of his unique talent.

His greatest extravagance was hospitality, of which I, too, had my share; often in the company, I am sorry to say, of men who after sitting at his board chose to speak of him and of his wife slightingly. Having some rudimentary sense of decency, their behaviour while actually under the Cranes' roof often produced on me a disagreeable impression. Once I ventured to say to him, "You are too good-natured, Stephen." He gave me one of his quiet smiles, that seemed to hint so poignantly at the vanity of all things, and after a period of silence remarked: "I am glad those Indians are gone." He was surrounded by men who, secretly envious, hostile to the real quality of his genius (and a little afraid of it), were also in antagonism with the essential fineness of his nature. But enough of them. *Pulvis et umbra sunt*. I mean even those that may be alive yet. They were ever hardly anything else; one would have forgotten them if it were not for the legend (if one may dignify perfidious and contemptible gossip by that name) they created in order to satisfy that same obscure instinct of base humanity, which in the past would often bring against any exceptional man the charge of consorting with the devil. It was just as vague, just as senseless, and in its implications just as lying as the mediæval kind. I have heard one of these "friends" hint before several other Philistines that Crane could not write his tales without getting drunk!

Putting aside the gross palpable stupidity of such a statement—which the creature gave out as an instance of the artistic temperament—I am in a position to disclose what may have been the foundation of this piece of gossip. I have seen repeatedly Crane at work. A small jug of still smaller ale would be brought into the study at about ten o'clock; Crane would pour out some of it into a glass and settle himself at the long table at which he used to write in Brede Place. I would take a book and settle myself at the other end of the same table, with my back to him; and for two hours or so not a sound would be heard in that room. At the end of that time Crane would say suddenly: "I won't do any more now, Joseph." He would have covered three of his large sheets with his regular, legible, perfectly controlled handwriting, with no more than a half-a-dozen erasures—mostly single words—in the whole lot. It seemed to me always a perfect miracle in the way of mastery over material and expression. Most of the ale would be still in the glass, and how flat by that time I don't like to think! The most amusing part was to see Crane, as if moved by some obscure sense of duty, drain the last drop of that untempting remnant before we left the room to stroll to and fro in front of the house while waiting for lunch. Such is the origin of some of these gleeful whispers making up the Crane legend of "unrestrained temperament." I have known various sorts of temperaments—some perfidious and some lying—

but "unrestrained temperament" is mere parrot talk.
It has no meaning. But it was suggestive. It was
founded on Crane's visits to town, during which I more
than once met him there. We used to spend afternoons
and evenings together, and I did not see any of his supposed revels in progress; nor yet have I ever detected
any after effects of them on any occasion. Neither have
I ever seen anybody who would own to having been a
partner in those excesses—if only to the extent of standing by charitably—which would have been a noble part
to play. I daresay all those "excesses" amounted to
very little more than the one in which he asked me to
join him in the following letter. It is the only note I
have kept from the very few which we exchanged. The
reader will see why it is one of my most carefully preserved possessions.

RAVENSBROOK, OXTED,
March 17 (1899).

MY DEAR CONRAD:

I am enclosing you a bit of MS. under the supposition
that you might like to keep it in remembrance of my
warm and endless friendship for you. I am still hoping
that you will consent to Stokes' invitation to come to
the Savage on Saturday night. Cannot you endure
it? Give my affectionate remembrances to Mrs.
Conrad and my love to the boy.

Yours always,
STEPHEN CRANE.

P. S. You must accept says Cora—and I—our
invitation to come home with me on Sat. night.

I joined him. We had a very amusing time with the
Savages. Afterwards Crane refused to go home till
the last train. Evidence of what somebody has called

his "unrestrained temperament," no doubt. So we went and sat at Gatti's, I believe—unless it was in a Bodega which existed then in that neighbourhood—and talked. I have a vivid memory of this awful debauch because it was on that evening that Crane told me of a subject for a story—a very exceptional thing for him to do. He called it "The Predecessor." I could not recall now by what capricious turns and odd associations of thought he reached the enthusiastic conclusion that it would make a good play, and that we must do it together. He wanted me to share in a certain success—"a dead sure thing," he said. His was an unrestrainedly generous temperament. But let that pass. I must have been specially predisposed, because I caught the infection at once. There and then we began to build up the masterpiece, interrupting each other eagerly, for, I don't know how it was, the air around us had suddenly grown thick with felicitous suggestions. We carried on this collaboration as far as the railway time-table would let us, and then made a break for the last train. Afterwards we did talk of our collaboration now and then, but no attempt at it was ever made. Crane had other stories to write; I was immersed deeply in "Lord Jim," of which I had to keep up the instalments in *Blackwood's;* difficulties in presenting the subject on the stage rose one after another before our experience. The general subject consisted in a man personating his "predecessor" (who had died) in the hope of winning a girl's heart. The scenes were to include a ranch at the foot of the Rocky Mountains, I remember, and the action, I fear, would have been frankly melodramatic. Crane insisted that one of the situations should present the man and the girl on a boundless plain standing by their dead ponies after a furious ride (a truly Crane touch). I made some

objections.   A boundless plain in the light of a sunset
could be got into a back-cloth, I admitted; but I
doubted whether we could induce the management of
any London theatre to deposit two stuffed horses on its
stage.

Recalling now those earnestly fantastic discussions,
it occurs to me that Crane and I must have been unconsciously penetrated by a prophetic sense of the
technique and of the very spirit of film-plays, of which
even the name was unknown then to the world.   But
if gifted with prophetic sense, we must have been
strangely ignorant of ourselves, since it must be
obvious to any one who has read a page of our writings
that a collaboration between us two could never have
come to anything in the end—could never even have
been begun.   The project was merely the expression of
our affection for each other.   We were fascinated for a
moment by the will-of-the-wisp of close artistic communion.   It would in no case have led us into a bog.   I
flatter myself we both had too much regard for each
other's gifts not to be clear-eyed about them.   We
would not have followed the lure very far.   At the
same time it cannot be denied that there were profound,
if not extensive, similitudes in our temperaments which
could create for a moment that fascinating illusion.
It is not to be regretted, for it had, at any rate, given us
some of the most light-hearted moments in the clear
but sober atmosphere of our intimacy.   From the force
of circumstances there could not be much sunshine in
it.   "None of them saw the colour of the sky!"   And
alas, it stood already written that it was the younger
man who would fail to make a landing through the surf.
So I am glad to have that episode to remember, a
brotherly serio-comic interlude, played under the
shadow of coming events.   But I would not have

alluded to it at all if it had not come out in the course
of my most interesting talk with the author of this
biography, that Crane had thought it worth while to
mention it in his correspondence, whether seriously or
humorously, I know not. So here it is without the
charm which it had for me, but which cannot be re-
produced in the mere relation of its outward characteristics: a clear gleam on us two, succeeded by the
Spanish-American War into which Crane disappeared
like a wilful man walking away into the depths of an
ominous twilight.

The cloudy afternoon when we two went rushing all
over London together was for him the beginning of the
end. The problem was to find £60 that day, before the
sun set, before dinner, before the "six-forty" train to
Oxted, at once, that instant—lest peace should be
declared and the opportunity of seeing a war be
missed. I had not £60 to lend him. Sixty shillings
was nearer my mark. We tried various offices but had
no luck, or rather we had the usual luck of money-
hunting enterprises. The man was either gone out to
see about a dog, or would take no interest in the
Spanish-American War. In one place the man wanted
to know what was the hurry? He would have liked
to have forty-eight hours to think the matter over. As
we came downstairs, Crane's white-faced excitement
frightened me. Finally it occurred to me to take him
to Messrs. William Blackwood & Sons' London office.
There he was received in a most friendly way. Presently
I escorted him to Charing Cross, where he took the
train for home with the assurance that he would have
the means to start "for the war" next day. That is
the reason I cannot to this day read his tale, "The Price
of the Harness", without a pang. It has done nothing
more deadly than pay his debt to Messrs. Blackwood;

yet now and then I feel as though that afternoon I had
led him by the hand to his doom. But, indeed, I was
only the blind agent of the fate that had him in her
grip! Nothing could have held him back. He was
ready to swim the ocean.

Thirteen years afterwards I made use, half consciously, of the shadow of the primary idea of "The
Predecessor" in one of my short tales which were
serialized in the *Metropolitan Magazine*. But in that
tale the dead man in the background is not a Predecessor but merely an assistant on a lonely plantation;
and instead of the ranch, the mountains, and the plains,
there is a cloud-capped island, a bird-haunted reef, and
the sea. All this the mere distorted shadow of what we
two used to talk about in a fantastic mood; but now and
then, as I wrote, I had the feeling that he had the right
to come and look over my shoulder. But he never
came. I received no suggestions from him, subtly
conveyed without words. There will never be any
collaboration for us now. But I wonder, were he alive,
whether he would be pleased with the tale. I don't
know. Perhaps not. Or, perhaps, after picking up
the volume with that detached air I remember so well
and turning over page after page in silence, he would
suddenly read aloud a line or two and then, looking
straight into my eyes as was his wont on such occasions,
say with all the intense earnestness of affection that was
in him: "I—like—that, Joseph."

HIS WAR BOOK

A Preface to Stephen Crane's "The Red Badge of Courage"

One of the most enduring memories of my literary life is the sensation produced by the appearance in 1895 of Crane's "Red Badge of Courage" in a small volume belonging to Mr. Heinemann's Pioneer Series of Modern Fiction—very modern fiction of that time, and upon the whole not devoid of merit. I have an idea the series was meant to give us shocks, and as far as my recollection goes there were, to use a term made familiar to all by another war, no "duds" in that small and lively bombardment. But Crane's work detonated on the mild din of that attack on our literary sensibilities with the impact and force of a twelve-inch shell charged with a very high explosive. Unexpected it fell amongst us; and its fall was followed by a great outcry.

Not of consternation, however. The energy of that projectile hurt nothing and no one (such was its good fortune), and delighted a good many. It delighted soldiers, men of letters, men in the street; it was welcomed by all lovers of personal expression as a genuine revelation, satisfying the curiosity of a world in which war and love have been subjects of song and story ever since the beginning of articulate speech.

Here we had an artist, a man not of experience but a man inspired, a seer with a gift for rendering the significant on the surface of things and with an incomparable insight into primitive emotions, who, in order to give us the image of war, had looked profoundly into his own breast. We welcomed him. As if the whole vocabulary of praise had been blown up sky-high by this missile from across the Atlantic, a rain of words descended on our heads, words well or ill chosen, chunks of pedantic praise and warm appreciation, clever words, and words of real understanding, platitudes, and felicities of criticism, but all as sincere in their response as the striking piece of work which set so many critical pens scurrying over the paper.

One of the most interesting, if not the most valuable, of printed criticisms was perhaps that of Mr. George Wyndham, soldier, man of the world, and in a sense a man of letters. He went into the whole question of war literature, at any rate during the nineteenth century, evoking comparisons with the *Mémoires* of General Marbot and the famous *Diary of a Cavalry Officer* as records of a personal experience. He rendered justice to the interest of what soldiers themselves could tell us, but confessed that to gratify the curiosity of the potential combatant who lurks in most men as to the picturesque aspects and emotional reactions of a battle we must go to the artist with his Heaven-given faculty of words at the service of his divination as to what the truth of things is and must be. He comes to the conclusion that:

"Mr. Crane has contrived a masterpiece."

"Contrived"—that word of disparaging sound is the last word I would have used in connection with any piece of work by Stephen Crane, who in his art (as indeed in his private life) was the least "contriving" of men. But as to "masterpiece," there is no doubt that "The Red Badge of Courage" is that, if only because of the marvellous accord of the vivid impressionistic description of action on that woodland battlefield, and the imaged style of the analysis of the emotions in the inward moral struggle going on in the breast of one individual—the Young Soldier of the book, the protagonist of the monodrama presented to us in an effortless succession of graphic and coloured phrases.

Stephen Crane places his Young Soldier in an untried regiment. And this is well contrived—if any contrivance there be in a spontaneous piece of work which seems to spurt and flow like a tapped stream from the depths of the writer's being. In order that the revelation should be complete, the Young Soldier has to be deprived of the moral support which he would have found in a tried body of men matured in achievement to the consciousness of its worth. His regiment had been tried by nothing but days of waiting for the order to move; so many days that it and the Youth within it have come to think of themselves as merely "a part of a vast blue demonstration." The army had been lying camped near a river, idle and fretting, till the moment when Stephen Crane lays hold of it at dawn with masterly simplicity: "The cold passed reluctantly from the earth. . . ." These are the first words of the war book which was to give him his crumb of fame.

The whole of that opening paragraph is wonderful in the homely dignity of the indicated lines of the landscape, and the shivering awakening of the army at the break of the day before the battle. In the next, with a most effective change to racy colloquialism of narrative, the action which motivates, sustains and feeds the inner drama forming the subject of the book, begins with the Tall Soldier going down to the river to wash his shirt. He returns waving his garment above his head. He had heard at fifth-hand from somebody that the army is going to move to-morrow. The only immediate effect of this piece of news is that a Negro teamster, who had been dancing a jig on a wooden box in a ring of laughing soldiers, finds himself suddenly deserted. He sits down mournfully. For the rest, the Tall Soldier's excitement is met by blank disbelief, profane grumbling, an invincible incredulity. But the regiment is somehow sobered. One feels it, though no symptoms can be noticed. It does not know what a battle is, neither does the Young Soldier. He retires from the babbling throng into what seems a rather comfortable dugout and lies down with his hands over his eyes to think. Thus the drama begins.

He perceives suddenly that he had looked upon wars as historical phenomenons of the past. He had never believed in war in his own country. It had been a sort of play affair. He had been drilled, inspected, marched for months, till he has despaired "of ever seeing a Greeklike struggle. Such were no more. Men were better or more timid. Secular and religious education had effaced the throat-grappling instinct, or else firm finance held in check the passions."

Very modern this touch. We can remember thoughts like these round about the year 1914. That Young Soldier is representative of mankind in more ways than one, and first of all in his ignorance. His regiment had listened to the tales of veterans, "tales of gray bewhiskered hordes chewing tobacco with unspeakable valour and sweeping along like the Huns." Still, he cannot put his faith in veterans' tales. Recruits were their prey. They talked of blood, fire, and sudden death, but much of it might have been lies. They were in no wise to be trusted. And the question arises before him whether he will or will not "run from a battle"? He does not know. He cannot know. A little panic fear enters his mind. He jumps up and asks himself aloud, "Good Lord, what's the matter

with me?" This is the first time his words are quoted,
on this day before the battle. He dreads not danger,
but fear itself. He stands before the unknown. He
would like to prove to himself by some reasoning
process that he will not "run from the battle." And in
his unblooded regiment he can find no help. He is
alone with the problem of courage.

In this he stands for the symbol of all untried men.

Some critics have estimated him a morbid case. I
cannot agree to that. The abnormal cases are of the
extremes; of those who crumple up at the first sight of
danger, and of those of whom their fellows say "He
doesn't know what fear is." Neither will I forget the
rare favourites of the gods whose fiery spirit is only
soothed by the fury and clamour of a battle. Of such
was General Picton of Peninsular fame. But the lot
of the mass of mankind is to know fear, the decent fear
of disgrace. Of such is the Young Soldier of "The Red
Badge of Courage." He only seems exceptional because he has got inside of him Stephen Crane's imagination, and is presented to us with the insight and the
power of expression of an artist whom a just and severe
critic, on a review of all his work, has called the fore-
most impressionist of his time; as Sterne was the
greatest impressionist, but in a different way, of his age.

This is a generalized, fundamental judgment. More
superficially both Zola's "La Débâcle" and Tolstoi's
"War and Peace" were mentioned by critics in connection with Crane's war book. But Zola's main
concern was with the downfall of the imperial régime
he fancied he was portraying; and in Tolstoi's book
the subtle presentation of Rostov's squadron under
fire for the first time is a mere episode lost in a mass
of other matter, like a handful of pebbles in a heap
of sand. I could not see the relevancy. Crane was

concerned with elemental truth only; and in any case I think that as an artist he is non-comparable. He dealt with what is enduring, and was the most detached of men.

That is why his book is short. Not quite two hundred pages. Gems are small. This monodrama, which happy inspiration or unerring instinct has led him to put before us in narrative form, is contained between the opening words I have already quoted and a phrase on page 194 of the English edition, which runs: "He had been to touch the great death, and found that, after all, it was but the great death. He was a man."

On these words the action ends. We are only given one glimpse of the victorious army at dusk, under the falling rain, "a procession of weary soldiers became a bedraggled train, despondent and muttering, marching with churning effort in a trough of liquid brown mud under a low wretched sky . . .", while the last ray of the sun falls on the river through a break in the leaden clouds.

This war book, so virile and so full of gentle sympathy, in which not a single declamatory sentiment defaces the genuine verbal felicity, welding analysis and description in a continuous fascination of individual style, had been hailed by the critics as the herald of a brilliant career. Crane himself very seldom alluded to it, and always with a wistful smile. Perhaps he was conscious that, like the mortally wounded Tall Soldier of his book, who, snatching at the air, staggers out into a field to meet his appointed death on the first day of battle—while the terrified Youth and the kind Tattered Soldier stand by silent, watching with awe "these ceremonies at the place of meeting"—it was his fate, too, to fall early in the fray.

JOHN GALSWORTHY

WHEN in the family's assembly at Timothy Forsyte's house there arose a discussion of Francie Forsyte's verses, Aunt Hester expressed her preference for the poetry of Shelley, Byron and Wordsworth, on the ground that, after reading the works of these poets, "one felt that one had read a book." And the reader of Mr. Galsworthy's latest volume of fiction, whether in accord or in difference with the author's view of his subject, would feel that he had read a book.

Beyond that impression one perceives how difficult it is to get critical hold of Mr. Galsworthy's work. He gives you no opening. Defending no obvious thesis, setting up no theory, offering no cheap panacea, appealing to no naked sentiment, the author of "The Man of Property" disdains also the effective device of attacking insidiously the actors of his own drama, or rather of his dramatic comedy. This is because he does not write for effect, though his writing will be found effective enough for all that. This book is of a disconcerting honesty, backed by a discouraging skill. There is not a single phrase in it written for the sake of its cleverness. Not one. Light of touch, though weighty in feeling, it gives the impression of verbal austerity, of a *willed* moderation of thought. The passages of high literary merit, so uniformly sustained as to escape the notice of the reader, expose the natural and logical development of the story with a purposeful progression which is primarily satisfying to the intelligence, and ends by stirring the emotions. In the essentials of matter and treatment it is a book of to-day. Its critical spirit and its impartial method are meant for a humanity which has outgrown the stage of fairy tales, realistic, romantic or even epic.

For the fairy tale, be it not ungratefully said, has walked the earth in many unchallenged disguises, and lingers amongst us to this day wearing, sometimes, amazingly heavy clothes. It lingers; and even it lingers with some assurance. Mankind has come of age, but the successive generations still demand artlessly to be amazed, moved and amused. Certain forms of innocent fun will never grow old, I suppose. But the secret of the long life of the fairy tale consists mainly in this, I suspect: that it is amusing to the writer thereof. Whatever public wants it supplies, it ministers first of all to his vanity in an intimate and delightful way. The pride of fanciful invention; the pride of that invention which soars (on goose's wings) into the empty blue is like the intoxication of an elixir sent by the gods above. And whether it is that the gods are unduly generous, or simply because the sight of human folly amuses their idle malice, that sort of felicity is easier attained pen in hand than the sober pride, always mingled with misgivings, of a single-minded observer and conscientious interpreter of reality. This is why the fairy tale, in its various disguises of optimism, pessimism, romanticism, naturalism and what not, will always be with us. And, indeed, that is very comprehensible; the seduction of irresponsible freedom is very great; and to be tied to the earth (even as the hewers of wood and drawers of water are tied to the earth) in the exercise of one's imagination, by every scruple of conscience and honour, may be considered a lot hard enough not to be lightly embraced. This is why novelists are comparatively rare. But we must not exaggerate

This world, even if one is tied fast to its earthy foundations by the subtle and tyrannical bonds of artistic conviction, is not such a bad place to write fiction in. At any rate, we can know of no other; an excellent reason for us to try to think as well as possible of the world we do know.

In this world, whose realities are discovered, interpreted, commented on, criticized and exposed in works of fiction, Mr. Galsworthy selects for the subject-matter of his book the Family, an institution which has been with us as long, I should think, as the oldest and the least venerable pattern of fairy tale. As Mr. Galsworthy, however, is no theorist but an observer, it is a definite kind of family that falls under his observation. It is the middle-class family; and even with more precision, as we are warned in the sub-title, an upper middle-class family anywhere at large in space and time, but a family; if not exactly of to-day, then of only last evening, so to say. Thus at the outset we are far removed from the vagueness of the traditional "once upon a time in a far country there was a king," which somehow always manages to peep through the solemn disguises of fairy tales masquerading as novels with and without purpose. The Forsytes walk the pavement of London and own some of London's houses. They wish to own more; they wish to own them all. And maybe they will. Time is on their side. The Forsytes never die— so Mr. Galsworthy tells us, while we watch them assembling in old Jolyon Forsyte's drawing room on the occasion of June Forsyte's engagement to Mr. Bosinney, incidentally an architect and an artist, but, by the only definition that matters, a man of no property whatever.

A family is not at first sight an alarming phenomenon. But Mr. Galsworthy looks at the Forsytes with the individual vision of a novelist seeking his inspiration amongst the realities of this earth. He points out to us this family's formidable character as a unit of society, as a reproduction in miniature of society itself. It is made formidable, he says, by the cohesion of its members (between whom there need not exist either affection or even sympathy) upon a concrete point, the possession of property.

The solidity of the foundation laid by Mr. Galsworthy for his fine piece of imaginative work becomes at once apparent. For whichever came first, family or property, in the beginnings of social organization, or whether they came together and were indeed at first scarcely distinguishable from each other, it is clear that in the close alliance of these two institutions society has found the way of its development and nurses the hope of its security. In their sense of property the Forsytes establish the consciousness of their right and the promise of their duration. It is an instinct, a primitive instinct. The practical faculty of the Forsytes has erected it into a principle; their idealism has expanded it into a sort of religion which has shaped their notions of happiness and decency, their prejudices, their piety, such thoughts as they happen to have and the very course of their passions. Life as a whole has come to be perceptible to them exclusively in terms of property. Preservation, acquisition—acquisition, preservation. Their laws, their morality, their art and their science appear to them, justifiably enough, consecrated to that double and unique end. It is the formula of their virtue.

In this world of Forsytes (who never die) organized in view of acquiring and preserving property, Mr. Galsworthy (who is no inventor of didactic fairy tales) places with the sure instinct of a novelist a man and a woman who are no Forsytes, it is true, but whom he

presents as in no sense the declared adversaries of the
great principle of property. They only happen to dis-
regard it. And this is a crime. They are simply two
people to whom life speaks imperatively in terms of
love. And this is enough to establish their irreconcil-
able antagonism and to precipitate their unavoidable
fate. Deprived naturally and suddenly of the support
of laws and morality, of all human countenance, and
even, in a manner of speaking, of the consolations of
religion, they find themselves miserably crushed, both
the woman and the man. And the principle of property
is vindicated. The woman being the weaker, it is in
her case vindicated with consummate cruelty. For a
peculiar cowardice is one of the characteristics of this
great and living principle. Strong in the worship of so
many thousands and in the possession of so many
millions, it starts with affright at the slightest challenge,
it trembles before mere indifference, it directs its
heaviest blows at the disinherited who should appear
weakest in its sight. Irene's fate is made unspeakably
atrocious, no less—but nothing more. Mr. Galsworthy's instinct and observation serve him well here.
In Soames Forsyte's town house, whose front door
stands wide open for half an hour or so on a certain
foggy night, there is no room for tragedy. It is one of
the temples of property, of a sort of unholy religion
whose fundamental dogma, public ceremonies and
awful secret rites, forming the subject matter of this
remarkable novel, take no account of human dignity.
Irene, as last seen crushed and alive within the hopeless
portals, remains for us a poignantly pitiful figure and
nothing more.

This then, roughly and summarily, is the book in
its general suggestion. Going on to particulars which
make up the intrinsic value of a work of art, it rests

upon the subtle and interdependent relation of Mr. Galsworthy's intellect and feelings which form his temperament, and reveals Mr. Galsworthy's very considerable talent as a writer—a talent so considerable that it commands at once our respectful attention. The foundation of this talent, it seems to me, lies in a remarkable power of ironic insight combined with an extremely keen and faithful eye for all the phenomena on the surface of the life he observes. These are the purveyors of his imagination, whose servant is a style clear, direct, sane, illumined by a perfectly unaffected sincerity. It is the style of a man whose sympathy with mankind is too genuine to allow him the smallest gratification of his vanity at the cost of his fellow creatures. In its moderation it is a style sufficiently pointed to carry deep his remorseless irony and grave enough to be the dignified vehicle of his profound compassion. Its sustained harmony is never interrupted by those bursts of cymbals and fifes which some deaf people acclaim for brilliance. Before all, it is a style well under control, and therefore it never betrays this tender and ironic writer into an odious cynicism of laughter or tears. For there are two kinds of cynicism, the cynicism of the hyena and the cynicism of the crocodile, which last, by the way, commands all sorts of respects from the inhabitants of these Isles. Mr. Galsworthy remains always a man, whether he is amused or moved.

I am afraid that my unavowed intention in writing about this book (of which I have talked so much and said so little) has been discovered by now. Therefore I confess. Confession—public, I mean—is good for one's conscience. Such is my intention. And it would be easier to carry out if I only knew exactly the motives which prompt people to read novels. But I do not know them all. Some of us, I understand, take up a novel to gratify a natural malevolence, the author being supposed to hold the mirror up to the odiously ridiculous nature of our next-door neighbour. From laboriously collected information I am, however, led to believe that most people read novels for amusement. This is as it should be. But, whatever be their motives, I entertain towards all novel-readers (for reasons which must remain concealed from the readers of this paper) the feelings of warm and respectful affection. I would not try to deceive them for worlds. Never! This being understood, I go on to declare, in the peace of my heart and the serenity of my conscience, that if they want amusement they will find it between the covers of this book. They will find plenty of it in this episode in the history of the Forsytes, where the reconciliation of a father and son, the dramatic and poignant comedy of Soames Forsyte's marital relations, and the tragedy of Bosinney's failure are exposed to our gaze with the remorseless yet sympathetic irony of Mr. Galsworthy's art, in the light of the unquenchable fire burning on the altar of property. They will find amusement, and perhaps also something more lasting—if they care for it. I say this with all the reserves and qualifications which strict truth requires around every statement of opinion. Mr. Galsworthy may possibly be found disappointing by some, but he will never be found futile by any one, and never uninteresting by the most exacting. I myself, for instance, am not so sure of Bosinney's tragedy. But this hesitation of my mind, for which the author may not be wholly responsible after all, need only be mentioned and no more, in the face of his considerable achievement.

A GLANCE AT TWO BOOKS

THE national English novelist seldom regards his work—the exercise of his Art—as an achievement of active life by which he will produce certain definite effects upon the emotions of his readers, but simply as an instinctive, often unreasoned, outpouring of his own emotions. He does not go about building up his book with a precise intention and a steady mind. It never occurs to him that a book is a deed, that the writing of it is an enterprise as much as the conquest of a colony. He has no such clear conception of his craft. Writing from a full heart, he liberates his soul for the satisfaction of his own sentiment; and when he has finished the scene he is at liberty to strike his forehead and exclaim: "This is genius!"

Thackeray is reported to have done this, and there is no reason why any novelist of his type should not. He is, as a matter of fact, writing lyrically (a lyric is the expression of a mood); he is expressing his own moods: I take what the gods give me—he says in all humility, and when the godhead inspires him with what seems good to his heart, to his imagination, to his tenderness or to his indignation, he may say, and use the words literally, "This is genius!"

It is. And it is probably the reason why the distinctively English novelist is always at his best in denunciations of institutions, of types or of conventionalized society.

It is comparatively easy for us, when we are really moved by the clearness of our vision, to convince an

132

audience that Messrs. A., B. and C. are callous, ferocious or cowardly. We should have to use much more conscious art to give a permanent impression of those gentlemen as purely altruist.

Thus Mr. Osborne, the hard merchant, father of Captain Osborne, is more definite and flawless than many of Thackeray's so-called good characters; and thus Mr. Pecksniff is, through scorn and dislike, rendered more memorable than the brothers Cheeryble. It is not perhaps so much that these distinguished writers were completely incapable of loving their fellow men simply as men, exposed to suffering, temptation and affliction, as that, neglecting the one indispensable thing, neglecting to use their powers of selection and observation, they emotionally excelled in rendering the disagreeable. And that is easy. To find beauty, grace, charm in the bitterness of truth is a graver task.

Thackeray, we imagine, did not love his gentle heroines. He did not love them. He was in love with the sentiments they represented. He was, in fact, in love with what does not exist—and that is why Amelia Osborne does not exist, either in colour, in shape, in grace, in goodness. Turgeniev probably did not love his Lisa, a most pathetic, pure, charming and profound creation, for what she was, in her creator's mind. He loved her disinterestedly, as it were, out of pure warmth of heart, as a human being in the tumult and hazard of life. And that is why we must feel, suffer and live with that wonderful creation. That is why she is as real to us as her stupid mother, as the men of the story, as the sombre Varvard, and all the others that may be called the unpleasant characters in "The House of Gentlefolk."

I have been reading two books in English which have attracted a good deal of intelligent attention, but neither seems to have been considered as attentively as they might have been from this point of view. The one, "The Island Pharisees," by Mr. John Galsworthy, is a very good example of the national novel: the other, "Green Mansions," by Mr. W. H. Hudson, is a proof that love, the pure love of rendering the external aspects of things, can exist side by side with the national novel in English letters.

Mr. Galsworthy's hero in "The Island Pharisees," during his pilgrimage right across the English social system, asks himself: "Why? Why is not the world better? Why are we all humbugs? Why is the social system so out of order?" And he gets no answer to his questions, for, indeed, in his mood no answer is possible, neither is an answer needed for the absolute value of the book. Shelton is dissatisfied with his own people, who are good people, with artists, whose "at homes" he drops into, with marriage settlements and wedding services, with cosmopolitan vagabonds, with Oxford dons, with policemen—with himself and his love.

The exposition of all the characters in the book is done with an almost unerring touch, with a touch indeed that recalls the sureness and the delicacy of Turgeniev's handling. They all live—and Mr. Galsworthy—or rather his hero, John Shelton, finds them all Pharisaic. It is as if he were championing against all these "good" people some intangible lost cause, some altruism, some higher truth that for ever seems to soar out of his grasp. It is not exactly that Shelton is made to uphold the bitter morality of the cosmopolitan vagabond; for Mr. Galsworthy is too good an artist and too good a philosopher to make his Louis Ferrand impossibly attractive or even possibly cynical.

Shelton upholds, not so much the fact as the ideal of honest revolt; he is the knight errant of a general idea.

Therein he ceases to resemble the other heroes of English fiction who are the champions of particular ideas, tilting sometimes at windmills (for the human power of self-deception is great), but with a particular foe always in their eye. Shelton distinctly does not couch his lance against a windmill. He is a knight errant, disarmed and faithful, riding forlorn to an inevitable defeat; his adversary is a giant of a thousand heads and a thousand arms, a monster at once perfectly human and altogether soulless. Though nobody dies in the book, it is really the record of a long and tragic adventure, whose tragedy is not so much in the event as in the very atmosphere, in the cold moral dusk in which the hero moves as if impelled by some fatal whisper, without a sword, corselet or helmet.

Amadis de Gaul would have struck a head off and counted it a doughty deed; Dickens would have flung himself upon pen and paper and made a caricature of the monster, would have flung at him an enormous joke vibrating with the stress of cheap emotions; Shelton, no legendary knight and being no humorist (but, like many simpler men, impelled by the destiny he carries within his breast), goes forth to be delivered, bound hand and foot, to the monster by his charming and limited Antonia. He is classed as an outsider by men in the best clubs, and his prospective mother-in-law tells him not to talk about things. He comes to grief socially, because in a world, which everyone is interested to go on calling the best of all possible worlds, he has insisted upon touching in challenge all the shields hung before all the comfortable tents: the immaculate shield of his fiancée, of his mother-in-law, of the best men in the best clubs. He gets himself called and thought of as Unsound; and there in his social world the monster has made an end of him.

This is the end of the book; and with it there comes
into the world of letters the beginning of Mr. Galsworthy as a novelist. For, paradoxically, a society
that could not stand a Hamlet in the flesh at any price
will read about him and welcome him on the stage to
the end of its own incorrigible existence. This book,
where each page lives with an interest of its own, has
for its only serious artistic defect that of not being
long enough, and for its greatest quality that of a sincere
feeling of compassionate regard for mankind expressed
nationally through a fine indignation. Of the promise
of its method, of the accomplished felicity of its phras-
ing, I have left myself no room to speak.

The innermost heart of "Green Mansions," which are
the forests of Mr. Hudson's book, is tender, is tranquil,
is steeped in that pure love of the external beauty of
things that seems to breathe upon us from the pages
of Turgeniev's work. The charming quietness of the
style soothes the hard irritation of our daily life in the
presence of a fine and sincere, of a deep and pellucid
personality. If the other book's gift is lyric, "Green
Mansions" comes to us with the tone of the elegy.
There are the voices of the birds, the shadows of the
forest leaves, the Indians gliding through them armed
with their blowpipes, the monkeys peering sadly from
above, the very spiders! The birds search for insects;
spiders hunt their prey.

"Now as I sat looking down on the leaves and the
small dancing shadow, scarcely thinking of what I was
looking at, I noticed a small spider with a flat body and
short legs creep cautiously out on to the upper surface
of a small leaf. Its pale red colour, barred with velvet
black, first drew my attention to it; for it was beautiful
to the eye. . . ."

"It was beautiful to the eye," so it drew the atten-

tion of Mr. Hudson's hero. In that phrase dwells the
very soul of the book whose voice is soothing like a soft
voice speaking steadily amongst the vivid changes of a
dream. Only you must note that the spider had come
to hunt its prey, having mistaken the small dancing
shadow for a fly, because it is there in the fundamental
difference of vision lies the difference between book
and book. The other type of novelist might say: "It
attracted my attention because it was savage and cruel
and beautiful only to the eye. And I have written of
it here so that it may be hated and laughed at for ever.
For of course being greedy and rapacious it was stupid
also, mistaking a shadow for substance, like certain evil
men, we have heard of, that go about crying up the
excellence of the world."

PREFACE

To "The Shorter Tales of Joseph Conrad"

THE idea of publishing a volume of selected stories has not been received without a good deal of hesitation on my part. So much in fact as to drive me into the dangerous attempt to disclose the state of the feelings with which I approach this explanatory preface. My hesitation was, I may say, of a private character; private in the sense of being rooted deep in my personality, and not easily explainable even to such good friends as it has been my fortune to find in the American public. The deep, complex (and at times even contradictory) feelings which make up the very essence of an author's attitude to his own creation are real enough, yet they may be, often are, but shapes of cherished illusions. Frail plants, you will admit, and fit only for the shade of solitary thought. Precious—perhaps? Yes. But by their very nature precious to only one man, to him in whose mind—or is it the heart?—they are rooted.

That consideration would seem to me conclusive against any one writing any preface whatever, if it were not for my ineradicable suspicion that in this world, which some philosophers have defined merely as a series of "vain appearances," our very illusions must have a practical meaning. Are they not as characteristic of an individual as his opinions, for instance, or the features of his face? In fact, being less controllable they must be even more dangerously revelatory. This is an alarming consideration. But whether because of a strain of native impudence, acquired callousness, or inborn trust in the goodness of human nature, it has not prevented me during the last few years from writing a good many revelatory prefaces, for which I have not been, so far, called to account. At any rate, no incensed man with a shotgun has yet called here to invite me to desist. Thus encouraged, here I am again volunteering yet one more of these sincere confessions.

To begin with, I may venture to affirm that, however spontaneous the initial impulse, not one of the stories from which those included in this volume have been selected was achieved without much conscious thought bearing not only on the problems of their style but upon their relation to life as I have known it, and on the nature of my reactions to the particular instances as well as to the general tenor of my personal experience. This gave to each of the successive tales, composed at various times and in varied mental conditions, a characteristic tone of its own. At least I thought so. Later, when I had to consider my past work in detail, in order to write the Author's Notes for my first collected edition, I was confirmed in my impression that each of my short-story volumes had a consistent unity of outlook covering the mingled subjects of civilization and wilderness, of land life and life on the sea.

It would not be too much to say that this trait would be apparent to the least critical of readers, in, for instance, the "Tales of Unrest." No story from that volume is included in this collection for a reason which will become apparent later to the patient reader of this Preface. It is the very first collection of short stories I ever published, with a range of scene including the Malay Archipelago, rustic Brittany, Central Africa, and the interior of an upper middle-class house in a residential street of London. It also seems to me perfectly clear on the face of it, that the volume called "A Set of Six"—from which one story has been selected for this book—is very different in its consistent mood of clear and detached presentation from any other volume of short stories which I have published before or after. Yet, in Time, it covers almost the whole of the nineteenth century; and in Space it moves from South America through England and Russia to end in the south of Italy. A benevolent critic has remarked to me privately that it was the least atmospheric of all my works; and from my point of view I accepted this as a tribute to that inner consistency which I would claim for every set of my shorter tales. In the same way in the case of the volume "Within the Tides" I take the opinion expressed by one of the reviewers: "that the whole of the book seemed to produce the impression of being greater than its component parts" as a confirmation of my sentiment of having welded the diversities of subject and treatment into a consistency characteristic, in its nature, of a certain period of my literary production.

The friendly reader will understand how, holding that belief on the subject of my shorter productions, I would recoil at first from taking any of my stories out of their appointed places in the group to which they originally belonged. And this the more because their grouping was never the result of a preconceived plan. It "just happened." And things that "just happen" in one's work seem impressive and valuable because they spring from sources profounder than the logic of a deliberate theory suggested by acquiring learning, let us say, or by lessons drawn from analysed practice. And no one need quarrel for such a view with an artist for whom self-expression must, by definition, be the principal object, if not the only *raison d'être*, of his existence. He will naturally take for his own, for better or worse, all the characteristics of his work; since all of them, intended or not intended, make up the individuality of his self-expression.

I suspect there are moments when what a man most values in his work—I mean even a man of action—is precisely the part the general mystery of things plays in its shaping: the discovery of those qualities that have "just happened" in that obscure region where honest success or honourable failure is unconsciously elaborated. But there are moments too when one's idealism (for idealism is practical and sane and the enemy of things that "just happen" and suchlike mysteries) prompts one to take up a different, more precise view of one's achievement—whatever it may be.

It must have been in one of those moments that the suggestion of a selected volume of my shorter stories came before me from my old friend and publisher, Mr. F. N. Doubleday, who is an idealist and who would simply hate to let anything "just happen" in his business. His business, to my mind, consists, mainly, in being the intermediary between certain men's reveries and the wide-awake brain of the rest of the world. Stated like this it seems a strangely fantastic occupation; yet his ways of carrying it on are always of a practical sort. I have learned to trust his conclusions implicitly on that ground. Also, for reasons of a deeper personal kind, having nothing to do with business, his words have great weight with me. But in order to reconcile my own idealism to the notion of taking the stories out of their natural surroundings, out of their native atmosphere as it were, some principle of selection had to be found. The only one that offered itself with any chance of being acceptable was the principle of classification by subject; one that, whatever its disadvantages, has at least the advantage of being immune from the infection of illusions.

But I soon found that for a writer whose simple purpose has ever been the sincere rendering of his own deeper and more sympathetic emotions in the face of his belief in men and things—the philosopher's "vain appearances" which yet have endured, poignant or amusing, for so many ages, moving processionally towards the End of the World, which when it comes will be the vainest thing of all—the principle was not so easy in its application as it seemed to be at first sight. Though I have been often classed as a writer of the sea I have always felt that I had no specialty in that or any other specific subject. It is true that I have found a full text of life on the sea, long before I thought of writing a line or even felt the faintest stirring towards self-expression by means of the printed word. Sea life had been my life. It had been my own self-sufficient, self-satisfying possession. When the change came over the spirit of my dream (Calderon said that "Life is a Dream") my past had, by the very force of my work, become one of the sources of what I may call, for want of a better word, my inspiration—of the inner force which sets the pen in motion. I would add here "for better or worse," if those words did not sound horribly ungrateful after so many proofs of sympathy from the public for which this particular Preface is destined.

As a matter of fact I have written of the sea very little if the pages were counted. It has been the scene, but very seldom the aim, of my endeavour. It is too late after all those years to try to keep back the truth; so I will confess here that when I launched my first paper boats in the days of my literary childhood, I aimed at an element as restless, as dangerous, as changeable as the sea, and even more vast;—the unappeasable ocean of human life. I trust this grandiloquent image will be accepted with an indulgent smile of the kind that is accorded to the lofty ambitions of well-meaning beginners. Much time has passed since, and I can assure my readers that I have never felt more humble than I do to-day while I sit tracing these words, and that I see now, more clearly than ever before, that indeed those were but paper boats, freighted with a grown-up child's dreams and launched innocently upon that terrible sea that, unlike the honest salt water of my early life, knows no hope of changing horizons but lies within the circle of an Eternal Shadow.

Approaching the problem of selection for this book in the full consciousness of my feelings, my concern was to give it some sort of unity, or in other words, its own character. Looking over the directive impulses of my writing life I discovered my guide in the one that had prompted me so often to deal with men whose existence was, so to speak, cast early upon the waters. Thus the characteristic trait of the stories included in this volume consists in the central figure of each being a seaman presented either in the relations of his professional life with his own kind, or in contact with landsmen and women, and embroiled in the affairs of that larger part of mankind which dwells on solid earth.

It would have been misleading to label those productions as sea tales. They deal with feelings of universal import, such, for instance, as the sustaining and inspiring sense of youth, or the support given by a stolid courage which confronts the unmeasurable force of an elemental fury simply as a thing that has got to be met and lived through with professional constancy. Of course, there is something more than mere ideas in those stories. I modestly hope that there are human

K

beings in them, and also the articulate appeal of their humanity so strangely constructed from inertia and restlessness, from weakness and from strength and many other interesting contradictions which affect their conduct, and in a certain sense are meant to give a colouring to the actual events of the tale, and even to the response which is expected from the reader. To call them "studies of seamen" would have been pretentious and even misleading, in view of the obscurity of the individuals and the private character of the incidents. "Shorter Tales" is yet the best title I can think of for this collection. It commends itself to me by its non-committal character, which will neither raise false hopes nor awaken blind antagonisms.

Why a volume aiming at unity should be wilfully divided into two parts is explained by my desire to give prominence to the stories which begin them: "Youth," which is certainly a piece of autobiography ("emotions remembered in tranquillity"), and "Typhoon," which, defined from a purely descriptive point of view, is the shorter of the two storm-pieces which I have written at different times.

From another point of view, the "guiding" point of view (that is of each story being concerned with a man who is also a seaman), the first part deals with younger and the second with older men. I hardly need say that in the arrangement of those two parts there has been no attempt at chronological order.

Therefore let neither friend nor enemy look for the development of the writer's literary faculty in this collection. As far as that is concerned, the book is a jumble. The unity of purpose lies elsewhere. In Part First, "Youth" speaks for itself, both in its triumphant feeling and in its wistful regrets. The second story deals with what may be called the "*esprit de corps*," the deep fellowship of two young seamen meeting for the first time. Those two tales may be regarded as purely professional. Of the other two in Part First, one, it must be confessed, is written round a ship rather than round a seaman. The last, trying to render the effect of the fascination of a roving life, has the hard lot of a woman for its principal interest.

Part Two deals with men of a more mature age. There is no denying that in the typhoon which is being wrestled with by Captain McWhirr, it is the typhoon that takes on almost a symbolic figure. The next story is the story of a married seaman, badly married I admit, whose humanity to a pathetic waif spoils his life for him. The third is the story of a swindle, to be frank, planned on shore, but the sympathetic person is a seaman all right. The last may be looked upon as a story of a seaman's love for a very silent girl; but what I tried partly to suggest there was the existence of certain straightforward characters combining a natural ruthlessness with an unexpected depth of moral delicacy. Falk obeys the law of self-preservation pitilessly; but at the crucial moment of his bizarre love story he will not condescend to dodge the truth—the horrid truth! Finally, let me say that with the exception of "Youth" none of these stories is a record of experience in the absolute sense of the word. As I have said before in another preface, they are all authentic because they are the product of twenty years of life—my own life. Deliberate invention had little to do with their existence—if they do exist. In each there lurks more than one intention. The facts gleaned from hearsay or experience in the various parts of the globe were but opportunities offered to the writer. What he has done with them is matter for a verdict which must be left to the individual consciences of the readers.

COOKERY

A Preface to "A Handbook of Cookery for a Small House," by Jessie Conrad

Of all the books produced since the most remote ages by human talents and industry those only that treat of cooking are, from a moral point of view, above suspicion. The intention of every other piece of prose may be discussed and even mistrusted; but the purpose of a cookery book is one and unmistakable. Its object can conceivably be no other than to increase the happiness of mankind.

This general consideration, and also a feeling of affectionate interest with which I am accustomed to view all the actions of the writer, prompt me to set down these few words of introduction for her book. Without making myself responsible for her teaching (I own that I find it impossible to read through a cookery book), I come forward modestly but gratefully as a Living Example of her practice. That practice I dare pronounce most successful. It has been for many priceless years adding to the sum of my daily happiness.

Good cooking is a moral agent. By good cooking I mean the conscientious preparation of the simple food of everyday life, not the more or less skilful concoction of idle feasts and rare dishes. Conscientious cookery is an enemy to gluttony. The trained delicacy of the palate, like a cultivated delicacy of sentiment, stands in the way of unseemly excesses. The decency of our life is for a great part a matter of good taste, of the

146

correct appreciation of what is fine in simplicity. The intimate influence of conscientious cooking by rendering easy the processes of digestion promotes the serenity of mind, the graciousness of thought, and that indulgent view of our neighbours' failings which is the only genuine form of optimism. Those are its titles to our reverence.

A great authority upon North American Indians accounted for the sombre and excessive ferocity characteristic of these savages by the theory that as a race they suffered from perpetual indigestion. The Noble Red Man was a mighty hunter but his wives had not mastered the art of conscientious cookery. And the consequences were deplorable. The Seven Nations around the Great Lakes and the Horse-tribes of the Plains were but one vast prey to raging dyspepsia. The Noble Red Men were great warriors, great orators, great masters of outdoor pursuits; but the domestic life of their wigwams was clouded by the morose irritability which follows the consumption of ill-cooked food. The gluttony of their indigestible feasts was a direct incentive to counsels of unreasonable violence. Victims of gloomy imaginings, they lived in abject submission to the wiles of a multitude of fraudulent medicine men—quacks—who haunted their existence with vain promises and false nostrums from the cradle to the grave.

It is to be remarked that the quack of modern civilization, the vendor of patent medicine, preys mainly upon the races of Anglo-Saxon stock who are also great warriors, great orators, mighty hunters, great masters of outdoor pursuits. No virtues will avail for happiness if the righteous art of cooking be neglected by the national conscience. We owe much to the fruitful meditations of our sages, but a sane view of life is, after all, elaborated mainly in the kitchen—the kitchen of the small house, the abode of the preponderant majority of the people. And a sane view of life excludes the belief in patent medicine. The conscientious cook is the natural enemy of the quack without a conscience; and thus his labours make for the honesty, and favour the amenity, of our existence. For a sane view of life can be no other than kindly and joyous, but a believer in patent medicine is steeped in the gloom of vague fears, the sombre attendants of disordered digestion.

Strong in this conviction, I introduce this little book to the inhabitants of the little houses who are the arbiters of the nation's destiny. Ignorant of the value of its methods, I have no doubt whatever as to its intention. It is highly moral. There cannot be the slightest question as to that; for is it not a cookery book? —the only product of the human mind altogether above suspicion.

In that respect no more need, or indeed can, be said. As regards the practical intention, I gather that no more than the clear and concise exposition of elementary principles has been the author's aim. And this too is laudable, because modesty is a becoming virtue in an artist. It remains for me only to express the hope that by correctness of practice and soundness of precept this little book will be able to add to the cheerfulness of nations.

THE FUTURE OF CONSTANTINOPLE

To the Editor of *The Times*, November 7, 1912.

SIR,

How long the last, Asiatic, phase of the history of the Turks—Sultanate of Damascus or Caliphate of Baghdad—may last, no one can say. That its European chapter is closed few only can doubt. But nobody will deny that a fierce scramble for Constantinople amongst the victors would be a most unseemly and disturbing complication.

The Serbs and Bulgars have no definite historical claim to advance. Greece has that, of course. But it must go very far back, to Byzantium—the old obscure colony. And really I cannot imagine this most democratic of kingdoms desiring a capital other than Athens —the very cradle of democracy, matchless in the wonders of its life and the vicissitudes of its history.

The Constantinople of which I think is not the Greek colony. It is the Imperial and symbolic city, one of the refuges of European civilization and the fit object of Europe's care. It should rest at last under the joint guarantee of all the Powers, after its infinitely varied, stormy, and tragic existence of august dominion, desperate wars, and abject slavery. It should find a dignified peace as an independent city, with a small territory, governed by an elected Senate (in which all the races of its population would be represented) and by—I won't call him its Burgomaster—let us say its

149

Patrician, as the executive head. The Balkan Powers might be co-jointly entrusted with his nomination. This would, to a certain extent, secure the share of Slavonic influence, since in the Senate the Greeks, I imagine, would predominate.

The independent Constantinople of my vision would be the splendid spiritual capital of the Balkan Peninsula naturally; its intellectual capital almost certainly. Commercially, too, as a free port, it would have all the chances, though Salonika may turn out a serious competitor. The various capitals of the Balkan States, residences of Courts and centres of political life, need not be jealous of the unique city which has done so much for the organization of mankind.

From its geographical position the Powers could easily give effective protection to that small municipal state. This plan, of course, implies free Dardanelles (but that seems already certain) and neutralized Bosphorus.

> I am, Sir,
> Your obedient servant,
> J. CONRAD.

November, 1912.

PERHAPS you will allow me to expand a little the idea thrown out in my letter to *The Times*. Of its reception at large I know nothing—and perhaps it does not merit any sort of reception. Of course, when one puts down anything in the shape of a proposal one does think over the objections. I am not inclined to believe a notion right and feasible simply because it has occurred to me. I am not of that happy temperament. Still, when the first man who read my letter turned upon me with the words, "So you too, I see, have joined the ideologues," I believe my cheek blanched.

This was a pretty heavy charge to bring against a man conscious of being guilty of no worse crime than a little imagination. But it was not the severity of the indictment nor yet the knowledge that "ideologue" was the term of utmost scorn in the mouth of Napoleon I which disturbed me. I was not frightened or angry. I was extremely surprised. Ideologue! And I had meant my suggestion to be eminently practical. Practical—that is, strictly in accordance with the fitness of things.

For to any one with a little historical sense it is not in the fitness of things that Constantinople should become the capital of a Bulgarian kingdom. I do not wish to hurt youthful susceptibilities but frankly the city of the Bosphorus is too great, too illustrious for that fate. The crash of its fall reëchoed ominously from one end of Christendom to the other. Its liberation will send a mournful whisper of angry dismay through the Mussulman world. And the event at which we look is historically too momentous for anything but the indestructible city itself, the jewel of the Balkans and once the only luminous spot through nearly five centuries of European night, to be its commemorative monument.

If this be mere ideology then I am safe to say it has its inciting cause in a perfectly clear view of possible eventualities. Let us piously hope that the dawn of peace for the Peninsula will succeed this lurid conflagration. The waned Crescent is setting for ever; but to a calm observer the dawn seems a long way yet below the horizon. There will be many questions to be settled between themselves by the Balkan Children of the Cross—not to speak of some other outside Christians with views of their own. And what if amongst other things we were to see before many years a war

*K

between Greece and Bulgaria for the possession of Constantinople?

For in fact, historically and racially, Greece alone has a claim to Constantinople. But who is going to hand it over to her now? The Bulgarians are nearer, and, we are given to understand, intoxicated with their success.

But in this success they are not alone; and you cannot cut the crown of victory into four pieces and present each combatant with one fourth of immortal glory. The only sane way is to leave the Imperial City outside the field of dispute by a guaranteed agreement. There will be spoil enough—whether cut and dried already or likely to turn out an awkward morsel to carve —to repay the blood and treasure. For as to risks taken, there were none to be proud of in this enterprise.

As to the difficulty of staying the conquering army, that is only the lofty verbiage of elation. A disciplined army can always be stayed. The Russian army was stayed at San Stefano, and its victory, if not so swift and more dearly bought, was quite as complete. And indeed I would not deny to any of the combatants the satisfaction of triumphal entry. It is what comes after that will count.

Let us be sincere in this matter. This game was played for unequal stakes. For Turkey was staking her very head, while the Allies risked no more than a more or less severe blood-letting. We know that if the fortune of war had gone the other way, unanimous Europe would have stopped it with the *status quo* declaration and the hand of Turkey would have been stayed. This fact, of which not a single Balkanian of them all ever had the slightest doubt, should make them amenable to reason in the final settlement.

Nobody wishes to rob them of what is won. Constantinople would remain a joint possession, but with a life and dignity of its own, till—till another Eastern Empire comes into being. And I think it would be a rational arrangement. The same objector, while I was trying to parry the charge of being an ideologue, lunged at me with the affirmation that this was "working for Russia." I confess that I don't understand that thrust. I think that for some time the possession of Constantinople has ceased to be one of the immediate aims of Russian policy. But even so, I don't see how I am serving any such dark purpose. It would be certainly easier to make war on Bulgaria and take Constantinople from it than to lay violent hands on a defenceless free town under a European guarantee, to which Russia herself would be a party. Not to mention the fact that such an aggression would be considered a *casus belli* not only by one but by all the Balkan powers (including Greece), the joint guardians of the city under Europe's sanction.

But as far as Russia's desire of an open Black Sea is concerned, the plan should certainly meet with her approval. I don't think that Russia would like to see numerous batteries of Bulgarian guns on the heights behind the town, sealing up the Bosphorus most effectually even without the help of the Turks on the other side. Indeed, I don't believe Russia would contemplate such a possibility for a moment. And how would Bulgaria (or Greece for that matter) like the obligation of an unarmed capital and the limitations of her sovereign rights in the matter of defence?

A neutralized Bosphorus and a free Constantinople would arouse no envy, no jealousies, and give no offence. Constantinople, a religious and intellectual capital—a common possession, giving no umbrage to any one—a holy city of infinite prestige and incom-

parable beauty. And I am even thinking here of the
Mohammedans. There will be, no doubt, many
Muslims left in the peninsula, industrious and peace-
able citizens of the Christian states. To them also
Constantinople shall be a holy city; for the religious
head of Mohammedans in Europe would be residing
there, nominated by the Caliph in Asia, subject to
confirmation by the Balkan powers.

It seems to me too that such a solution of the Con-
stantinople problem would soothe to a certain extent
the grief and unrest of Mussulmans all the world over.
A consideration worth the notice of the European
States which have become by conquest masters of
Mohammedan territories.

The details of organization, in which all the races of
the peninsula would be justly represented, cannot be a
matter of insuperable difficulty. Every Bulgarian,
Greek, Serb, or Montenegrin entering Constantinople
should be able to say: "I am at home here. This
ground on which I stand has been liberated by me and
my brothers and this Imperial City, free to us all and
subject to no one, is the splendid monument of our
victory."

THE CONGO DIARY

INTRODUCTION

THE diary kept by Joseph Conrad in the Congo in 1890, or such of it as has survived (for there is no saying whether there was more or not), is contained in two small black penny notebooks, and is written in pencil. One carries his initials, J. C. K.—Joseph Conrad Korzeniowski. The first entry is dated June 13, 1890, but in the second notebook dates are practically discarded, and it is impossible to say when the last entry was made. And names of places, also, are practically discarded in the second notebook, while abounding in the first, so that, though we can see that the diary was begun at Matadi, we cannot discover where it was ended. The last place mentioned is Lulanga, far up the great sweep of the Congo River to the north of the Equator, but there remain some twenty-four pages of the diary beyond that entry in which no name whatsoever appears. It must, indeed, have been continued into the very heart of that immense darkness where the crisis of his story, "Heart of Darkness," is unfolded. We know from "A Personal Record" that he reached ultimately somewhere to the neighbourhood of Stanley Falls; and Stanley Falls are farther from Lulanga than Lulanga is from Stanley Pool.

And it is in this same book that we can read how the Polish boy, when nine years of age, looking upon a map of Africa, had put his finger upon its unexplored centre, and had said to himself, "When I grow up I shall go *there*." Go there he did, and these notebooks are the first expression of his fulfilled resolve.

The map will enable the reader to plot out, with reasonable accuracy, the exact route followed by Conrad on his overland journey, from Matadi, which is about one hundred miles above the mouth of the Congo, to Nselemba, on or near the southeast corner of Stanley Pool—a distance of probably more than two hundred and fifty miles from Matadi—where it was that he joined the *Roi des Belges*, as second in command, for the up-river voyage. The places and streams alluded to on this overland journey have been given on the map in Conrad's own spelling, even where their names have been altered (unless beyond recognition, which may have happened in certain instances) in existing atlases, many of which have been examined, or can only be placed approximately, owing to their not being mentioned at all. The mapping of the Congo is not in a very advanced state, and, what with the paucity of the entries and the contradictory nature of the information, precise accuracy is not attainable. All the same, it is easy enough to trace the general line of his march, which lay much nearer the banks of the Congo than lies the railway which now runs between Matadi and Kinshasa on Stanley Pool.

The following is a reproduction of the first notebook alone—not, however, of the list of names, persons, books, stores, and the calculations that fill the last pages—consisting of thirty-two manuscript pages, not all of which are full, and twelve of which are further curtailed by Conrad's sectional drawings of the day's march. The given spelling and abbreviations have been adhered to throughout—they help to heighten its true flavour—but the paragraphing and the punctuation have been freely altered.

I may mention that these two notebooks are now preserved in the library of Harvard University, and

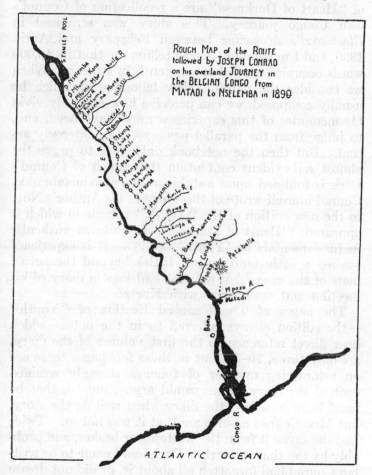

ROUGH MAP of the ROUTE
followed by JOSEPH CONRAD
on his overland JOURNEY in
the BELGIAN CONGO from
MATADI to NSELEMBA in 1890

that when I was in America in 1925 I saw them again in their new and permanent home and checked the text once more.

As to the appended footnotes, their chief purpose has been to show how closely some of the earlier pages of "Heart of Darkness" are a recollection of Conrad's own Congo journey. This story was serialized in *Blackwood's Magazine* between February and April, 1899, and I remember Conrad telling me that its 40,000 words occupied only about a month in writing. When we consider the painful, slow labour with which he usually composed, we can perceive how intensely vivid his memories of this experience must have been, and, to judge from the parallel passages, how intensely actual. But then the notebook only goes to prove the almost self-evident contention that much of Conrad's work is founded upon autobiographical remembrance. Conrad himself wrote of this story in his Author's Note to the new edition of the "Youth" volume in which it appeared: "'Heart of Darkness' is quite as authentic in fundamentals as 'Youth' . . . it is experience pushed a little (and only a little) beyond the actual facts of the case." If only he had kept a diary of his meeting and association with Kurtz!

The pages of The Concord Edition of "Youth" —the edition always referred to in the notes—which bear direct reference to the first volume of the diary, are only three, 70–72, but in these few pages there are an astonishing number of touches strongly reminiscent of the diary. One would argue, indeed, that he must have consulted the diary when writing the story, but Mrs. Conrad assures me that it was not so. Twice had she saved it from the wastepaper basket, and probably by the time "Heart of Darkness" came to be written Conrad had forgotten all about it, or did not dream that it had survived. He never spoke to me of it, and I never heard of its existence until after his death.

The second notebook, which is an entirely technical

account of Congo navigation, written, no doubt, in relation to the then river charts, is not printed here, simply because it has no personal or literary interest. It is much longer than the first notebook, and is contained on seventy-nine pages, apart from several pages of rough outline maps. I reproduce a portion of one page, in order to show a sample:

"11. N. (A) Long reach to a curved point. Great quantity of dangerous snags along the star[d] shore. Follow the slight bend of the shore with caution. The Middle of the Channel is a S—B— [sand bank] always covered. The more northerly of the two islands has its lower end bare of trees covered with grass and light green low bushes, then a low flat, and the upper end is timbered with light trees of a darker green tint."

It will be seen from this passage, which, though typical, is less technical than most, that the second notebook is not really, like the first, so much in the nature of a diary as of a specific aid to navigation. But those who recall the river journey in "Heart of Darkness," with its dangers and its difficulties, will perceive how this notebook, too, has played its special and impersonal part in the construction of that story.

The title-page of the first notebook is almost all torn out, but the title-page of the second reads, "Up-river Book, commenced 3 August 1890, S.S. *Roi des Belges*." Long ago, when I was making, from Conrad's dictation, a list of the ships he had sailed in, he wrote opposite *Roi des Belges*—"'Heart of Darkness,' 'Out-post.'" And, in truth, hints for "Heart of Darkness," reminders of "Heart of Darkness," lie thick upon the pages of the first notebook, though "An Outpost of Progress"—"the lightest part of the loot I carried off from Central

Africa," to quote his Author's Note to "Tales of Unrest," in which it was published—is only visible in the diary by the implication of the tropical African atmosphere.

No other diary of Conrad's is extant, and I am very sceptical as to whether he ever kept another. He was not at all that type of man, and his piercing memory for essentials was quite sufficient for him to recreate powerfully vanished scenes and figures for the purposes of his work. In 1890, of course, he had published nothing, and though we know that the unfinished MS. (seven chapters) of "Almayer's Folly" accompanied him on his Congo journey—"A Personal Record" describes how it was nearly lost on the river—yet it is doubtful whether he seriously envisaged its appearance in print at a future date. It was largely the breakdown of Conrad's health, due to this very trip, that caused him finally to abandon the sea, and if he had not abandoned the sea, how could he have become a novelist in the accepted sense? Unless we assume that genius must always find means of full expression—a big assumption and quite beyond proof—we owe it really to an accident that Conrad adopted writing as a career. Without this journey, and, therefore, without this diary, where would have been the great Conrad novels?

Thirty-four years to a day from beginning the second notebook, Conrad died—August 3, 1924. Reading it again, I find, as I am continually finding, how many things there are which I would have liked to ask him and never did ask him, and how much I want to know, which I never now can know. Well, that is always what happens when our friends depart. This diary is only a strange, tantalizing fragment and must eternally remain so. Yet it has a value of its own, both real and romantic, and I am glad to be able to give it to the world.

RICHARD CURLE.

THE DIARY

Arrived at Matadi[1] on the 13th of June, 1890.

Mr. Gosse, chief of the station (O. K.) retaining us for some reason of his own.

Made the acquaintance of Mr. Roger Casement,[2] which I should consider as a great pleasure under any circumstances and now it becomes a positive piece of luck. Thinks, speaks well, most intelligent and very sympathetic.

Feel considerably in doubt about the future. Think just now that my life amongst the people (white) around here cannot be very comfortable. Intend avoid acquaintances as much as possible.

Through Mr. R. C. have made the acquain^{ce} of Mr. Underwood, the Manager of the English Factory (Hatton & Cookson) in Kalla Kalla. Av^u com^l—hearty and kind. Lunched there on the 21st.

24th. Gosse and R. C. gone with a large lot of ivory down to Boma. On G.['s] return intend to start up the river. Have been myself busy packing ivory in casks. Idiotic employment. Health good up to now.

Wrote to Simpson, to Gov. B., to Purd.,[3] to Hope,[4]

---

[1] On his voyage from Europe presumably.

[2] Afterwards the notorious Sir Roger Casement, who was hanged for treason on August 3, 1916—the very date on which Conrad died eight years later. At this period Casement was in the employ of a commercial firm in the Congo. In 1898 he became British Consul in the Congo Free State.

[3] Probably Captain Purdy, an acquaintance of Conrad.

[4] Conrad's old friend, now living in Essex, Mr. G. F. W. Hope. In 1900 Conrad dedicated "Lord Jim" to Mr. and Mrs. Hope, "with grateful affection after many years of friendship."

to Capt. Froud,[1] and to Mar.[2]. Prominent characteristic of the social life here; people speaking ill of each other.[3]

Saturday, 28th June. Left Matadi with Mr. Harou[4] and a caravan of 31 men.[5] Parted with Casement in a very friendly manner. Mr. Gosse saw us off as far as the State station.

First halt, M'poso. 2 Danes in Company.[6]

Sund[ay], 29th. Ascent of Pataballa sufficiently fatiguing. Camped at 11 A.M. at Nsoke river. Mosquitos [always spelt thus].

Monday, 30th. To Congo da Lemba after passing black rocks. Long ascent. Harou giving up.[7] Bother. Camp bad. Water far. Dirty. At night Harou better.

Tuesday, 1st July. Left early in a heavy mist, marching towards Lufu river. Part route through forest on the sharp slope of a high mountain. Very long descent. Then market place from where short

---

[1] The then Secretary of the London Ship-Master's Society. See "A Personal Record" (Concord Edition), p. 7. "Dear Captain Froud—it is impossible not to pay him the tribute of affectionate familiarity at this distance of years—had very sound views as to the advancement of knowledge and status for the whole body of the officers of the mercantile marine."

[2] Probably Marguerite Poradowska, his aunt.

[3] This was also a failing of the white men at the "Central Station" in "Heart of Darkness."

[4] Harou was an official of the Etat Indépendant du Congo Belge.

[5] Compare "Heart of Darkness," p. 70: "Next day I left that station at last with a caravan of 60 men for a 200-mile tramp." On 13 out of the 19 travelling days taken by Conrad on this overland journey he kept a record of the distance covered, and it totals 197½ miles.

[6] Curiously enough, the identity of these two Danes was discovered by Monsieur G. Jean-Aubry in Brussels early in 1925. Not knowing that they were mentioned in the diary, he omitted to take names or particulars.

[7] He seems to have been constantly unwell and one may compare "Heart of Darkness," p. 71: "I had a white companion too, not a bad chap, but rather too fleshy, and with the exasperating habit of fainting on the hot hillsides, miles away from the least bit of shade or water."

walk to the bridge (good) and camp. V. G. Bath. Clear river. Feel well. Harou all right. 1st chicken, 2 P. [M.] No sunshine to-day.

Wednesday, 2nd July. Started at 5:30 after a sleepless night. Country more open. Gently undulating hills. Road good, in perfect order. (District of Lukungu.) Great market at 9:30. Bought eggs and chickens. Feel not well to-day. Heavy cold in the head. Arrived at 11 at Banza Manteka. Camped on the market place. Not well enough to call on the missionary. Water scarce and bad. Camp^g place dirty. 2 Danes still in Company.

Thursday, 3rd July. Left at 6 A. M. after a good night's rest. Crossed a low range of hills and entered a broad valley, or rather plain, with a break in the middle. Met an off^er of the State inspecting. A few minutes afterwards saw at a camp^g place the dead body of a Backongo. Shot?[1] Horrid smell.

Crossed a range of mountains, running N. W.—S. E. by a low pass. Another broad flat valley with a deep ravine through the centre. Clay and gravel. Another range parallel to the first mentioned, with a chain of low foothills running close to it. Between the two came to camp on the banks of the Luinzono river. Camp^g place clean. River clear. Gov^t Zanzibari[2] with register. Canoe. 2 Danes camp^g on the other bank. Health good.

General tone of landscape gray-yellowish (dry grass)

---

[1]Compare "Heart of Darkness," p. 71: "Once a white man in an unbuttoned uniform camping on the path . . . was looking after the upkeep of the road, he declared. Can't say I saw any road or any upkeep, unless the body of a middle-aged negro with a bullet-hole in the forehead, upon which I absolutely stumbled three miles further on, may be considered as a permanent improvement."

[2]Compare "Heart of Darkness," p. 71, in which he mentioned his meeting with a white man, who was accompanied by "an armed escort of lank Zanzibaris."

with reddish patches (soil) and clumps of dark green vegetation scattered sparsely about. Mostly in steep gorges between the high mountains or in ravines cutting the plain.[1]

Noticed Palma Christi—Oil Palm. Very straight, tall and thick trees in some places. Name not known to me. Villages quite invisible. Infer their existence from calbashes [sic] suspended to palm trees for the "Malafu." Good many caravans and travellers. No women, unless on the market place.

Bird notes charming. One especially a flute-like note. Another, kind of "boom" ressembling [sic] the very distant baying of a hound. Saw only pigeons and a few green parroquets. Very small and not many. No birds of prey seen by me.[2]

Up to 9 A. M. sky clouded and calm. Afterwards gentle breeze from the Nth generally and sky clearing. Nights damp and cool. White mists on the hills up about half way. Water effects very beautiful this morning. Mists generally raising before sky clears.

Distance 15 miles. General direction N. N. E.— S. S. W.

Friday, 4th July. Left camp at 6 A. M. after a very unpleasant night. Marching across a chain of hills and then in a maze of hills. At 8:15 opened out into an undulating plain. Took bearings of a break in the chain of mountains on the other side. Bearing N. N. E. Road passes through that. Sharp ascents up very steep hills not very high. The higher mountains recede sharply and show a low hilly country. At 9:30 market

---

[1] In "Heart of Darkness," p. 70, the country of the march is described as "a stamped-in network of paths spreading over the empty land, through long grass, through burnt grass, through thickets, down and up hilly ravines, up and down stony hills ablaze with heat."

[2] These natural history observations are curious, as Conrad practically never showed the slightest interest in such subjects.

place. At 10 passed R. Lukanga and at 10:30 camped on the Mpwe R.

To-day's march. Direction N. N. E.½.—N. Dist[ce] 13 miles.

Saw another dead body lying by the path in an attitude of meditative repose.[1]

In the evening three women, of whom one albino, passed our camp; horrid chalky white with pink blotches; red eyes; red hair; features very negroid and ugly. Mosquitos. At night when the moon rose heard shouts and drumming in distant villages.[2] Passed a bad night.

Saturday, 5th July. Left at 6:15. Morning cool, even cold, and very damp. Sky densely overcast. Gentle breeze from N. E. Road through a narrow plain up to R. Kwilu. Swift flowing and deep, 50 yds. wide. Passed in canoes. After[ds] up and down very steep hills intersected by deep ravines. Main chain of heights running mostly N. W.—S. E. or W. and E. at times. Stopped at Manyamba. Camp[g] place bad—in a hollow—water very indifferent. Tent set at 10:15. N. N. E. Dist[ce] 12 m.

To-day fell into a muddy puddle—beastly! The fault of the man that carried me. After camp[g] went to a small stream, bathed and washed clothes. Getting jolly well sick of this fun.

To-morrow expect a long march to get to Nsona, 2 days from Manyanga. No sunshine to-day.

Sunday, 6th July. Started at 5:40. The route at first hilly, then, after a sharp descent, traversing a

---

[1] The most "Conradesque" phrase in the diary.

[2] Compare "Heart of Darkness," p. 71: "Perhaps on some quiet night the tremor of far-off drums, sinking, swelling, a tremor vast, faint; a sound weird, appealing, suggestive, and wild—and perhaps with as profound a meaning as the sound of bells in a Christian country."

broad plain. At the end of it a large market place. At 10 sun came out. After leaving the market passed another plain, then, walking on the crest of a chain of hills, passed 2 villages and at 11 arrived at Nsona. Village invisible.

Direction about N. N. E. Distance 18 miles.

In this camp (Nsona) there is a good camp^g place. Shady, water far and not very good. This night no mosquitos owing to large fires, lit all round our tent. Afternoon very close: night clear and starry.

Monday, 7th July. Left at 6, after a good night's rest, on the road to Inkandu, which is some distance past Lukunga Govt. station. Route very accidented.[1] Succession of round steep hills. At times walking along the crest of a chain of hills. Just before Lukunga our carriers took a wide sweep to the southward till the station bore Nth. Walking through long grass for 1½ hours. Crossed a broad river about 100 feet wide and 4 deep.

After another ½ hour's walk through manioc plantations in good order rejoined our route to the E^d of the Lukunga sta^{on}, walking along an undulating plain towards the Inkandu market on a hill. Hot, thirsty and tired. At 11 arrived on the m^{ket} place. About 200 people. Business brisk. No water; no camp^g place. After remaining for one hour left in search of a resting place. Row with carriers. No water. At last about 1½ P. M. camped on an exposed hill side near a muddy creek. No shade. Tent on a slope. Sun heavy. Wretched.

Direction N. E. by N.—Distance 22 miles.

Night miserably cold. No sleep. Mosquitos.

Tuesday, 8th July. Left at 6 A. M. About ten

---

[1] An odd Gallicism. Conrad knew French long before he knew English; moreover, he was naturally talking much French at this time.

minutes from camp left main Gov^t path for the Manyanga track. Sky overcast. Rode up and down
all the time, passing a couple of villages. The country
presents a confused wilderness of hills, landslips on their
sides showing red. Fine effect of red hill covered in
places by dark green vegetation. ½ hour before beginning the descent got a glimpse of the Congo. Sky
clouded.

To-day's march—3 h. General direction N. by E.
Dist^cc 9½ miles.

Arrived at Manyanga at 9 A. M. Received most
kindly by Messrs. Heyn and Jaeger. Most comfortable
and pleasant halt.

Stayed here till the 25. Both have been sick. Most
kindly care taken of us. Leave with sincere regrets.

Friday, the 25th July, 1890. Left Manyanga at 2½
P. M. with plenty of hammock carriers. H. lame
and not in very good form. Myself ditto but not lame.
Walked as far as Mafiela and camped—2 h.

Saturday, 26th. Left very early. Road ascending
all the time. Passed villages. Country seems thickly
inhabited. At 11 arrived at large market place. Left
at noon and camped at 1 P. M.

General direction E ½ N-W ½ S. Sun visible at 8 A. M.
Very hot. Distance 18 miles.

Sunday, 27th. Left at 8 A. M. Sent luggage carriers
straight on to Luasi, and went ourselves round by the
Mission of Sutili. Hospitable reception by Mrs.
Comber. All the missio. absent. The looks of the
whole establishment eminently civilized and very
refreshing to see after the lots of tumbled down hovels
in which the State & Company agents are content to
live. Fine buildings. Position on a hill. Rather
breezy.

Left at 3 P. M. At the first heavy ascent met Mr.

Davis, Miss., returning from a preaching trip. Rev. Bentley away in the south with his wife. This being off the road, no section given.[1]

Distance traversed about 15 miles. Gen. direction E. N. E.

At Luasi we get on again on to the Gov' road.

Camped at 4½ P. M. with Mr. Heche in company. To-day no sunshine. Wind remarkably cold. Gloomy day.

Monday, 28th. Left camp at 6:30 after breakfasting with Heche. Road at first hilly. Then walking along the ridges of hill chains with valleys on both sides. The country more open and there is much more trees[2] growing in large clumps in the ravines.

Passed Nzungi and camped, 11, on the right bank of the Ngoma, a rapid little river with rocky bed. Village on a hill to the right.

General direction E. N. E.—Distance 14 miles.

No sunshine. Gloomy cold day. Squalls.

Tuesday, 29th. Left camp at 7, after a good night's rest. Continuous ascent; rather easy at first. Crossed wooded ravines and the river Lunzadi by a very decent bridge. At 9 met Mr. Louette escorting a sick agent of the comp'ʸ back to Matadi. Looking very well. Bad news from up the river. All the steamers disabled—one wrecked.[3] Country wooded. At 10:30 camped at Inkissi.

---

[1]Sections of the day's marches, with numerous names on them, were given under the following dates: July 3rd, 4th, 5th, 6th, 7th, 8th, 25th, 28th, 29th, 30th, 31st, August 1st.

[2]One of the few un-English phrases in the diary. By 1890 Conrad had been a British subject for six years, but he never learnt the language until he was grown up.

[3]Compare "Heart of Darkness," p. 72: "One of them [the white men at the Central Station] . . . informed me with great volubility and many digressions . . . that my steamer was at the bottom of the river."

General direction E. N. E.—Dist^ce 15 miles.

Sun visible at 6:30.   Very warm day.

Inkissi River very rapid; is about 100 yards broad.   Passage in canoes.   Banks wooded very densely, and valley of the river rather deep, but very narrow.

To-day did not set the tent, but put up in Gov^t shimbek. Zanzibari[1] in charge—very obliging. Met ripe pineapple for the first time. On the road to-day passed a skeleton tied up to a post. Also white man's grave—no name—heap of stones in the form of a cross. Health good now.

Wednesday, 30th.   Left at 6 A. M. intending to camp at Kinfumu. Two hours sharp walk brought me to Nsona na Nsefe. Market. ½ hour after Harou arrived very ill with billious [*sic*] attack and fever. Laid him down in Gov^t shimbek.

Dose of ipec^a.   Vomiting bile in enormous quantities. At 11 gave him 1 gramme of quinine and lots of hot tea. Hot fit ending in heavy perspiration. At 2 P. M. put him in hammock and started for Kinfumu. Row with carriers all the way.[2] Harou suffering much through the jerks of the hammock. Camped at a small stream. At 4 Harou better; fever gone.

General direction N. E. by E. ½ E. Distance 13 miles.

Up till noon sky clouded and strong N. W. wind very chilling. From 1 P. M. to 4 P. M. sky clear and a very hot day. Expect lots of bother with carriers to-morrow. Had them all called and made a speech,

---

[1]See note, p. 163.

[2]Compare "Heart of Darkness," p. 71: "Then he [the white man with him] got fever, and had to be carried in a hammock slung under a pole. As he weighed sixteen stone I had no end of rows with the carriers."

which they did not understand.[1] They promise good behaviour.

Thursday, 31st. Left at 6. Sent Harou ahead, and followed in ½ an hour.[2]

Road presents several sharp ascents, and a few others easier but rather long. Notice in places sandy surface soil instead of hard clay as heretofore; think however that the layer of sand is not very thick and that the clay would be found under it. Great difficulty in carrying Harou. Too heavy—bother![3] Made two long halts to rest the carriers. Country wooded in valleys and on many of the ridges.

At 2:30 P. M. reached Luila at last, and camped on right bank. Breeze from S. W.

General direction of march about N. E. ½ E. Distance, est^d 16 miles.

Congo very narrow and rapid. Kinzilu rushing in. A short distance up from the mouth, fine waterfall. Sun rose red. From 9 A. M. infernally hot day. Harou very little better. Self rather seedy. Bathed. Luila about 60 feet wide. Shallow.

Friday, 1st of August, 1890. Left at 6:30 A. M. after a very indifferently passed night. Cold, heavy mists. Road in long ascents and sharp dips all the way to Mfumu Mbé. After leaving there, a long and painful climb up a very steep hill; then a long descent to Mfumu Kono, where a long halt was made. Left at 12:30 P. M. towards Nselemba. Many ascents. The aspect of the country entirely changed. Wooded hills

---

[1]Compare "Heart of Darkness," p. 71: ". . . one evening, I made a speech in English with gestures, not one of which was lost to the sixty pairs of eyes before me."

[2]Compare "Heart of Darkness," pp. 71–2: ". . . the next morning I started the hammock off in front all right."

[3]Compare "Heart of Darkness," p. 71: ". . . he [the white man with him] weighed sixteen stone. . . ."

with openings.   Path almost all the afternoon thro' a forest of light trees with dense undergrowth.

After a halt on a wooded hillside, reached Nselemba at 4:10 P. M.   Put up at Gov^t shanty.   Row between the carriers and a man, stating himself in Gov^t employ, about a mat.   Blows with sticks raining hard.   Stopped it.

Chief came with a youth about 13 suffering from gun-shot wound in the head.   Bullet entered about an inch above the right eyebrow, and came out a little inside the roots of the hair, fairly in the middle of the brow in a line with the bridge of the nose.   Bone not damaged apparently.   Gave him a little glycerine to put on the wound made by the bullet on coming out.

Harou not very well.   Mosquitos—frogs—beastly! Glad to see the end of this stupid tramp.   Feel rather seedy.   Sun rose red.   Very hot day.   Wind S^th.

General direction of march N. E. by N.   Distance about 17 miles.[1]

---

[1]The journey from Matadi to this point by Stanley Pool took nineteen travelling days.   Compare "Heart of Darkness," p. 72: "On the fifteenth day I came in sight of the big river [Congo] again and hobbled into the Central Station."

THE END

JOSEPH CONRAD

Born at Berdiczew, Poland, 3rd December 1857;
christened Józef Teodor Konrad Naleçz Korzeniowski.
Travelled to Marseilles, 1874, and became a seaman,
first reaching England in 1878. Became a naturalized
British subject, and obtained Master Mariner's
Certificate, 1886. Married Miss Jessie George,
1896; two sons: Borys (*b.* 1898), John (*b.* 1906).
Died at Bishopsbourne, Kent, 3rd August 1924.

SELECT BIBLIOGRAPHY

JOSEPH CONRAD'S WORKS

(1) 1895   *Almayer's Folly—A Story of an Eastern River.*
(2) 1896   *An Outcast of the Islands.*
(3) 1897   *The Nigger of the 'Narcissus'—A Tale of the Sea.* (First
            edition to include Preface, 1914.)
(1) 1898   *Tales of Unrest.* (Contents: 'Karain, a Memory,' 'The
            Idiots,' 'An Outpost of Progress,' 'The Return,' 'The
            Lagoon.')
(4) 1900   *Lord Jim—A Tale.*
(5) 1902   *Youth: A Narrative; and Two Other Stories.* (Contents:
            'Youth,' 'Heart of Darkness,' 'The End of the Tether.')
(3) 1903   *Typhoon, and Other Stories.* (Contents: 'Typhoon,' 'Amy
            Foster,' 'Falk,' 'To-morrow.')
(6) 1903   *Romance—A Novel.* (In collaboration with Ford Madox
            Hueffer.)
(7) 1904   *Nostromo—A Tale of the Seaboard.*
(8) 1906   *The Mirror of the Sea—Memories and Impressions.*
(9) 1907   *The Secret Agent—A Simple Tale.*
(10) 1908   *A Set of Six.* (Contents: 'Gaspar Ruiz,' 'The Informer,'
            'The Brute,' 'An Anarchist,' 'The Duel,' 'Il Conde.')
(11) 1911   *Under Western Eyes.*
(8) 1912   *A Personal Record.* (First published under the title *Some*
            Reminiscences.)
(12) 1912   *'Twixt Land and Sea—Tales.* (Contents: 'A Smile of For-
            tune,' 'The Secret Sharer,' 'Freya of the Seven Isles.')
(13) 1913   *Chance—A Tale in Two Parts.*
(14) 1915   *Victory—An Island Tale.*
(15) 1915   *Within the Tides—Tales.* (Contents: 'The Planter of
            Malata,' 'The Partner,' 'The Inn of the Two Witches,'
            'Because of the Dollars.')
(15) 1917   *The Shadow Line—A Confession.*
(16) 1919   *The Arrow of Gold—A Story between Two Notes.*
(17) 1920   *The Rescue—A Romance of the Shallows.*
(18) 1921   *Notes On Life and Letters.* (Essays, mainly from periodicals;
            thirteen in Part I on Letters, and thirteen in Part II on Life.)
(19) 1923   *The Rover.*
(20) 1925   *Suspense—A Napoleonic Novel.*

SELECT BIBLIOGRAPHY

(21) 1925   *Tales of Hearsay*. (Contents: 'The Warrior's Soul,' 'Prince Roman,' 'The Tale,' 'The Black Mate.')

(21) 1926   *Last Essays*. (Nineteen essays, uncollected in book form at the time of his death.)

1923–8   Uniform Edition of the Works of Joseph Conrad, with an Author's Note to each volume.

(Reissued as Collected Edition, 1946–54, 21 volumes. The numbers against the titles in the above list show where two works are contained in one volume in the Collected Edition.)

LETTERS

The Life and Letters of Joseph Conrad (2 vols.), edited by G. Jean-Aubry, 1927. *Letters from Joseph Conrad, 1895–1924*, edited, with an Introduction, by Edward Garnett, 1928. *Letters from Joseph Conrad to Richard Curle*, 1928. *Letters of Joseph Conrad to Marguerite Poradowska*, New York, 1940. *Joseph Conrad: Letters to William Blackwood and David S. Meldrum*, edited by W. Blackburn, 1959.

BIOGRAPHICAL AND CRITICAL WRITINGS ON CONRAD

Joseph Conrad, A Study, by Richard Curle, 1914. Essay in *Notes on Novelists*, by Henry James, 1914. *Joseph Conrad*, by Hugh Walpole, 1916. Essay on Conrad in *A Book of Prefaces*, by H. L. Mencken, 1917. *Joseph Conrad, A Personal Remembrance*, by Ford Madox Ford, 1924. Essay on Conrad in *The Common Reader*, by Virginia Woolf, 1925. *Joseph Conrad as I knew Him*, by Jessie Conrad, 1926. 'Reminiscences of Conrad' and 'Preface to Conrad's Plays' in *Castles in Spain*, by John Galsworthy, 1927. *The Last Twelve Years of Joseph Conrad*, by Richard Curle, 1928. *The Polish Heritage of Joseph Conrad*, by Gustav Morf, 1930. *Joseph Conrad's Mind and Method*, by R. L. Mégroz, 1931. *Joseph Conrad and His Circle*, by Jessie Conrad, 1936. *Joseph Conrad, Some Aspects of the Art of the Novel*, by Edward Crankshaw, 1936. Introductory Essay by Edward Garnett to *Conrad's Prefaces to his Works*, 1937. *Joseph Conrad, the Making of a Novelist*, by John D. Gordan, 1940. *Joseph Conrad, England's Polish Genius*, by M. C. Bradbrook, 1941. Introduction by A. J. Hoppé to *The Conrad Companion*, 1946. *The Great Tradition* (George Eliot, Henry James, and Joseph Conrad), by F. R. Leavis, 1948. *Joseph Conrad*, by Oliver Warner, 1951. *Conrad, a Re-assessment*, by D. Hewitt, 1952. *Six Great Novelists*, by Walter Allen, 1955 (Conrad is the sixth subject). *The Mirror of Conrad*, by E. H. Visiak, 1955. *The Sea Dreamer: Life of Conrad*, by G. Jean-Aubry, 1957. *Joseph Conrad*, by Thomas Moser, 1957. Essay on Conrad in *The Fine Art of Reading*, by Lord David Cecil, 1957. *Joseph Conrad, A Study in Non-conformity*, by Osborn Andreas, 1959. *Joseph Conrad, A Critical Biography*, by Jocelyn Baines, 1960.

BIBLIOGRAPHIES

A Bibliography of the Writings of Joseph Conrad, 1895–1921, by T. J. Wise, 1921. *A Conrad Memorial Library*, collected by G. T. Keating, New York, 1929, with 'Check List of Additions,' 1938. *Joseph Conrad at Mid-Century, Editions and Studies, 1895–1955*, by K. A. Lohf and E. P. Sheehy, 1959.